Make Music With
Queen

Complete Lyrics / Guitar Chord Boxes / Chord Symbols
Fifteen classic songs with a foreword by Stevie Chick

Published 2002

© International Music Publications Ltd
Griffin House 161 Hammersmith Road London W6 8BS England

Editor: Chris Harvey
Foreword: Stevie Chick
Design: Dominic Brookman
Music arranged and engraved by: Artemis Music Ltd
Cover Photograph © 2002 Richard E Aaron / Redferns Mus
All other photography © 2002 S&G, David Redfern, Richard   s Music Picture Library

Foreword

Sometimes gaudy, sometimes just glam, mostly great; Queen's gift for rock 'n' roll curios and deftly-tailored anthems saw them snatch the heavy-rock crown for perpetuity.

While it's hard to imagine a rock'n'roll world without Queen, it's harder still to think of any bands they've truly influenced in the years since the mighty **Killer Queen** first announced their singular presence. Oh sure, there are plenty of bands who will openly or ironically admit to loving Queen, and there are a fair few artists whose embrace of the more baroque and elaborate flavours of rock betray more than a few adolescent hours spent worshipping at the altar of Brian May's home-made hearth-sprung guitar magnificence (but these same artists are often too cool to admit the influence). But can you actually name any single band who've truly embraced the entire diverse, nay, (brilliantly) ridiculous jumble of colour, sound and whimsy that was Queen, since their tragic enforced abdication?

We're talking about a band who would sequence Sabbath-on-steroidal-mogadon heaviness between gospel-flecked soul and Pimms-and-cucumber-sandwiches Noel Coward-esque musicalia on chart-dominating, multi-platinum-winning albums. We're talking about a band whose frontman could prance about in black leather with a thick 'tache across his top lip while lasciviously discussing his bisexuality in an accent thick with camp while finding his music embraced by the less-than-enlightened and certainly gay-unfriendly rock heartlands. We're talking about a band who could top the charts with opulent seven-minute rock-operettas, and then crossover to black American radio at the height of that country's cultural segregation with a bass line so badass it would form the spine of one of hip-hop's most legendary formative cuts.

No, there won't ever be another band like Queen. They revolutionized rock'n'roll marketing and artistry with their innovative, legendary, often-hilarious videos. They rocked hard while possessing a complex and uniquely un-rock sense of humour. They weathered numerous sea-changes of taste and fashion to establish a reach far beyond just rock fans - their greatest hits albums staples in many a record collection. They were a remarkable, unrepeatable phenomenon; this is their story, these are their songs...

Unlike most rock'n'roll stars' legends (but closer to the truth of most rockers' upbringings), the boys who made up Queen hailed from inarguably sedate middle class backgrounds. That the band never made any attempt to hide this fact might explain why they were held up for so much contempt by the (more often than not middle-class themselves) music press, especially during the hey-day of punk-rock (itself mostly the preserve and product of middle-class art-school subversives).

Indeed, the band's acceptance of their not-uncomfortable place in England's still subtly rigid class system explains their ease with the variety of different influences coursing through their music, as does their essential Englishness. From the Beatles beyond, British rock'n'roll music has, to a certain degree, remained the preserve of the enthusiast; there is a sense, right or wrong, that the true wellsprings of rock'n'roll can be located within the verdant deltas and cold-hearted cities of America. That an English (or indeed any non-American) musician's appreciation of rock'n'roll will be that of a student of the music, whereas an American musician is playing the folk music of his nation (which is, in itself, a problematic issue involving ever-more circular arguments regarding the racial/social segregation of the United States and broader issues of cultural ownership, all of which could fill the pages of books heavier, drier and less-readable than this here tome).

American artists play from the heart, is the suggestion, whereas for British artists rock'n'roll is a more intellectual, contrived activity; the flipside of this is that America's rock'n'roll audience has a much lower tolerance of and appetite for irony, where British rock'n'roll has always been characterised by a sense of humour, of the elements of ridiculousness, inherent in rock'n'roll, a more playful approach to the music which embodies both affection for it, and a certain distance which allows a different perspective. And while Queen rocked hard enough to charm the American markets, for a while at least, they also had that distance which allowed them the playfulness which gave birth to the impressive hybrids which marked their career.

Queen's music had a campness beyond their lead-singer's sexuality, beyond the gaudy transvestism of the glam-rock movement their entrance into the world coincided with, but which their ambitions and abilities swiftly outgrew. For Freddie Mercury, rock'n'roll was just another cloak to be donned in a series of impressive costume changes; sure, this outfit may have fit the singer better than any other, but the flamboyance and larger-than-life personality of the man and his band ensured that he wore the clothes, the clothes didn't wear him.

Look back at the various personae Mercury took on throughout Queen's neon-tipped period at the top: from leotard-clad prog-pop pixie, through black leather rock toy, through Barishnikov-esque ballet boy, through moustachioed macho man, to the rock'n'roll yuppie conservatism of the band's last couple of albums (not to mention the countless, even more outrageous costumes Freddie donned for their various videos). Each should've jarred with the other, but Queen's dilettante-esque eclecticism came from the *heart*, so all these varied visions of what rock'n'pop could be all made some crazy sense in terms of the band's own broad embrace of music, and the band's own patchwork make up.

There was flamboyant Freddie, the insecure young schoolboy whose father's civil service job meant he moved about from city to city throughout his childhood, the ugly duckling later blossoming into a monster of self-confidence and supernatural ease before hundreds of thousands of adoring fans. There was Brian, the scholarly guitar nerd who was something of a musical prodigy as a child; who famously fashioned his guitar, with the aid of his father, from an old mahogany fireplace, a knitting needle, mother of pearl buttons and parts of an old motor bike; and whose symphonic swoops of guitar are as instantly recognisable as Freddie's olympic larynx. There was Roger, the rock'n'roll playboy on the drumkit, who provided the laddish glamour the band required through the rock'n'roll heyday. And there was John Deacon, the rocksteady bassist whose cool demeanour suited that of the man who watched over the band's financial affairs. Somehow they gelled together and made up one of the sturdiest, longest-lasting line-ups in rock's turbulent history. What they shared in common - besides their strong friendship, and a united sense of hunger for rock stardom and excellence - was their passion for music, and the peculiarly British sense of humour which accompanied this.

With their middle-class roots, the rabid vagabond muse of rock'n'roll should've been elusive, but this didn't mean they didn't *love* it with all their hearts, and it didn't prevent them from making a mean, fierce noise of their own, which made a nonsense of such barriers (from the early, lusted howls of **Tie Your Mother Down**, to the more mature but no less ferocious sturm und drang of **Was It All Worth It** Queen could kick a riff as hard as you please). They shared a similar, admiring distance from the high-brow artistic impulses they managed to pull close to their besequinned bosoms, be it cod-operatic bombast, or pinched, genteel high-camp whimsy.

And it was, doubtless, this very artistic itinerancy, drawing on the 'artifice' root of 'art', that so infuriated music critics of the time; the NME went as far as to ask whether Freddie Mercury was a 'prat' (their opinion - yes). Rock criticism loves heroes like Bob Dylan, whose every utterance drips with supposed profundity, whose serious artist-ness yields column after column of pseudo-literary criticism and sixth-form poetry discussion class-type dissection. Queen were more about pose than composure, fun over furrowed-brow pretension. It was impossible to locate Freddie's 'heart' in the grand guignols of Queen's music, at least until the very end; in the same way most rock stars' music reveals chunks of their secret selves. Queen seemed 'fakes' to some, 'impersonal' to others, even 'fascistic' to Rolling Stone's reviewer of the **Jazz** album.

But to audiences the world over, Queen's very grandness was their gift, and songs like **Love Of My Life** not only moved these very audiences, but moved them to sing along, in imperfect note but with perfect volume, at live shows (indeed, the song would gain a life of its own on the road, as the sublime **Queen: Live Killers** album proves). And within their very eclecticism, and the wit and humour of their videos, lays a sense of displacement and of a sweeping passion which is ever repressed in traditional English life; stifled, tucked away into the darker reaches of the psyche where it boils away, unchecked, brewing the kind of epic, hilarious, life-affirming rock-baroques Queen served up for the world.

But Queen weren't to the throne born. No, there were periods of struggle, of anonymity, before their coronation, including numerous faltering stabs at stardom before taking the name Queen, and two albums which languished in relative obscurity until the band's success shed light on their qualities.

All the members of Queen had been pursuing assorted rockin' concerns throughout the 60s; Brian May's first band was an outfit called 1984, featuring a fellow student at Hampton Grammar school, Tim Staffell, on vocal duties. 1984 disbanded as its members entered academia, but Tim and Brian

maintain their musical connection, May taking a degree in Physics and Maths at Imperial College, while Staffell studied at Ealing College Of Art, where he met a young Freddie Bulsara. Roger Taylor, meanwhile, shifts his passions from guitar to the drums and reluctantly takes his place on a dental course at London Hospital Medical School.

But Roger's heart simply isn't in orthodontistry, and by 1968 he has dropped out, sharing a flat with Bulsara in Shepherds Bush and manning a stall in Kensington market with the young art student. All is not doom and gloom for Roger, however; a year previous, answering an advertisement placed on the Imperial College noticeboard, he joins a nascent outfit tentatively called Smile, featuring Tim Staffell on bass/vocals, and Brian May on guitar. May similarly puts his love of rock before his academic career; receiving an honours degree, he subsequently declines a prestigious offer to work at the Jodrell Bank Laboratory, choosing instead to further his doctorate studies at Imperial and keep Smile alive.

The band had swiftly garnered a glowing reputation for their progressive rock grandeur, gigs infamously catching the band stretching their coterie of covers through endless improvised contortions. Their musicianship was certainly never in doubt, as the trio handled tempo changes and complex flurries of notes with admirable aplomb. But while the band's prog-flavoured explorations won them a loyal following on the London circuit of student unions and pub back-rooms they called their own, there was little to differentiate these hirsute pop mastodons from the platoons of guitar-toting hairies then taking rock into ever more-complex, less-glamorous directions.

After a disastrous 1969 signing to Mercury Records - the result of which is one single, **Earth** (b/w **Step On Me**), released only in the United States - the band's collective spirits take a tumble. The trio return to their studies, Roger taking an abortive course in Biology at North London Polytechnic, followed by Botany at Kew Gardens, wary of the machinations of a music industry which has already clipped their wings, while being aware that, if they're ever to escape their insalubrious rock'n'roll surroundings, they'll have to tussle with the thorny beasts of the record labels again at some point.

The situation certainly got the better of Staffell, who departed the band in the Summer of 1970, for the oddly-named Humpy Bong. While this group took Staffell onto the hallowed boards of TV's Top Of The Pops, they progressed no further. But Staffell's exit from Smile set the scene for the entrance of the grand dame of rock'n'roll... Freddie Mercury, as Bulsara was now known, had been fronting local rock'n'roll band Wreckage, and was piecing together his dreams of a flamboyant, extravagant rock'n'roll which would splice together his heavy rock'n'pop fixations - being a huge fan of Led Zeppelin, The Beatles and, most of all, Jimi Hendrix - and his tastes for the, ahem, finer pursuits. It was Mercury who approached May and Taylor with the idea of changing the band's name to 'Queen'; sceptical at first, Mercury's charisma soon won them over.

By the following February, the final piece of Queen's jigsaw was about to fall into place. Mild-mannered John Deacon had been playing bass in any number of R&B bands for past few years, despite being a good couple of years younger than his new bandmates. Quietly-spoken, the least flamboyant member of the band, Deacon would ultimately contribute some of the best-loved tunes in the Queen catalogue, and his sturdy bass lines would gel with Taylor's titanic drumbreaks to form one of the sleekest, most dependable rhythm sections in British rock'n'roll.

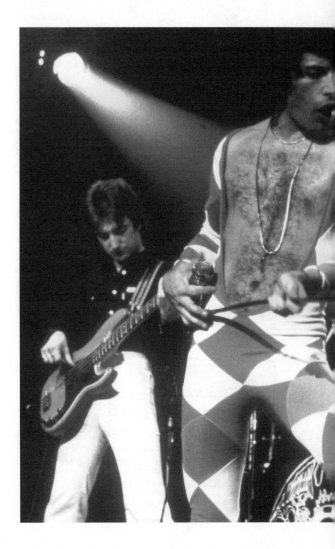

Queen soon began to play private shows, trying out their new material and giving Mercury the opportunity to explore his ideas for stagecraft before friendly audiences. While he had yet to don the leotards and other such costuming which would make the band legendary, they certainly conducted themselves with a little more flair than the heavy-rock scene of the time, which was swiftly becoming very self-involved and unglamourous, as the progressive noise of late-60s rock'n'roll coagulated into two prongs: the starchy prog-rock movement, and the bleak, neanderthal heavy metal hordes. While Queen would draw some inspiration from these movements, and share fans in their ranks, they would ultimately develop a pop nous which would rocket them from these margins.

But their initial material was certainly of the heavy, progressive variety, although still impressive enough to catch the ear of John Anthony, a talent scout for production company Trident Studios in Spring of 1972. Queen were demoing tracks at De Lane Lea studios for free, in return for demonstrating the studio's newest equipment. Anthony, accompanied by producer Roy Thomas Baker, was only visiting the studio for such a demonstration, but was most impressed by Queen's potential; unsurprisingly, really, since he'd been the producer of Smile's abortive first single. Anthony brought Queen to Trident's attention, and they swiftly signed the band, who returned to the studio to record their debut album, with Baker at the helm.

Sessions were long, problematic and arduous, as the album was recorded

4

on downtime at the studio. But by the end of 1972, the album was complete, and Trident shopped the band around the record labels. EMI ultimately picked the band up, and released the album in a blaze of publicity in the Summer of 1973. A suite of heavy rock and ethereal ballads, Queen's eponymous debut boasted one single, the glam-rock stomp of 'Keep Yourself Alive', remarkable mostly for the band's blend of pop-rock lightness and May's symphonic multi-tracked guitar majesty. BBC Radio refused to playlist the single, but the band soon became firm favourites of the station's progressive wing, which commissioned exclusive sessions and live performances from the band.

This trend continued with 'Queen 2', which followed in early 1974. A much more confident and coherent album, it is considered by Queen aficionados - Smashing Pumpkins' Billy Corgan among them - as one of the band's best. Dark, heavy and foreboding, it hits number 5 in the charts, while **Seven Seas Of Rhye**, the preceding single, hits number 10 and sees the band make their inaugural performance on Top Of The Pops. But just when their career seemed to be taking off, disaster strikes, albeit an ultimately fortuitous brand of disaster. Brian is laid low with hepatitis in May 1974 while the band are supporting Mott The Hoople in New York. A UK tour later that year is cancelled, and the band choose instead to hit the studio.

The album, prompted by their illness-enforced road exile, will be the record which makes household names of Queen, and will lay the groundwork for a decade and a half of chart domination.

Sid Vicious: You reckon you're bringing Ballet to the masses, dontcha?
Freddie Mercury: That's right, Mr Terrible.

[possibly apocryphal meeting between Sid Vicious and Freddie Mercury, backstage at Top Of The Pops, 1977]

If there were any recurring motifs in the criticism which greeted Queen's early long-player excursions, they were the accusations of creative predictability, that the band were merely aping Led Zeppelin or the Glam Rock boom of the times. And while these criticisms weren't all that valid, it certainly wasn't until **Sheer Heart Attack** that Queen grew into their unmistakable sound.

Produced by the band and Roy Thomas Baker, **Sheer Heart Attack** opened with the sublime **Brighton Rock** - breathless glam-rock lusting from a falsetto-rising Freddie, swooping full-band harmonies and some mind-blowing guitar explorations from Brian, hard-rock and pure-pop all at once - and then proceeded to gad about from fragile chamber ballads (**Lily Of The Valley**) to full-on thrash-rock (**Stone Cold Crazy**) to cod-20s flapper-jazz (**Bring Back That Leroy Brown**) to opiated S&M pop (**She Makes Me**) in less than 45 minutes, all with an inimitable confidence, verve and humour.

But while the album also gave us the diamond-edged glam-operetta **Now I'm Here**, it's lead single was the deathless hit, **Killer Queen**. This was the song which won Queen the radiowaves and the nation's hearts, taking the wicked glam poise of 'Ride A White Swan'-era T-Rex, and then allying it with May's chromium guitar leads and the kind of overdriven psychedelic phasing the band's idol Hendrix wasn't averse to in his prime. But from the opening finger-clicks, the song is all Freddie's; in his lilting tales of diplomatic excess, wielding a subtle, camp bitchiness like a stiletto-knife - "Her perfumes came naturally from Paris / (naturally!) / Because she couldn't care less".

After tours of Japan, America and Europe, plus a couple more ecstatically-received jaunts across the UK, the band return to the studio to record the follow-up to **Sheer Heart Attack**. They knew they had to pull out all of the stops to top that album; the resultant recording sessions would yield what is widely-regarded as the band's masterpiece album, and certainly the band's most (in)famous and best-loved single.

A Night At The Opera marked the cessation of the band's working relationship with Trident studios, a sundering still surrounded with legal murk. The band chose to voice those frustrations with **Death On Two Legs**, the band's opening track and a further progression in the band's symphonic glam-rock sound. As with **Sheer Heart Attack**, the selection of songs is dizzyingly eclectic and further displays the band's confidence in their identity; sure, the album might take in proggy metallic epics like **The Prophet's Song** - many multi-tracked Freddies singing in rounds with each other in between huge walls of wrought-iron guitar rock - along with dainty love troths like **Love Of My Life** and the camper-than-a-row-of-tents **Lazing On A Sunday Afternoon**. But all these songs worked together to create a sound uniquely Queen's. It wasn't just the breadth of styles which characterised the band, it was their lightness of touch, their wit, their head-spinning chutzpah; and, of course, their outstanding musical contributions.

A Night At The Opera featured two of Queen's most enduring songs. **You're My Best Friend** was something of a stylistic departure, even for Queen. From its tolling, warm Rhodes keyboard opening notes, to its melodicism and sunshine backing harmonies, the track owed much to classic soul music, albeit given the Queen twist in the form of Brian's guitar sheen and Freddie's relatively-restrained vocal gymnastics. It wouldn't be the last time John Deacon would reach back into his love of 'black' music to find inspiration for Queen's biggest hits.

A Night At The Opera's other huge hit soon became Queen's signature tune, and a byword for the band's grandiose ambitions and even grander sweep. Bohemian Rhapsody was a miracle of studio production, a behemoth of a song - six minutes long - which somehow became one of the least-likely, but most-beloved hit singles in rock history, thanks in no small part to its influential pop-video - mistakenly believed by many to be the first in the genre - and the dedication of DJ, TV star and friend of the band Kenny Everett, who was handed a copy of the single by Freddie on the proviso he wouldn't play it on his show, and who proceeded to play it, in its entirety, fourteen times over the next two days.

A genius Frankenstein's monster of a single, Bo Rhap - as it would become known - encapsulated Queen. Opening with multi-tracked choral harmonies cooing a gossamer-thin melody, segueing into some bittersweet Freddie-led piano'n'vocal ennui, which builds dramatically until dropping into the shockingly-audacious operatic mid-section, multi-tracked Queens howling hysterically, nonsensically, until the song slams into the full-on headbangathon of its penultimate passage, before melting back into the heartbreakingly tear-stained Freddie'n'piano coda. Everything that made the band special was captured, or at least glimpsed upon, within those six minutes. It was a triumph. It was genius. It was an unalloyed success.

And it would prove to be difficult to follow. Opera and Bo Rhap made global superstars of Queen, and they toured heavily, accordingly. Then, in September of 1976 they entered the studio to record the album's sequel. A Day At The Races similarly took its title from an old Marx Brothers movie, took as its sleeve artwork a negative mirror of the previous album's cover, and echoed its predecessor in style and pace many ways. Which is not to denigrate what is a *great* rock'n'roll album. But A Day At The Races so closely associates itself with its world-beating ancestor it can't help but suffer by comparison. It has some great tunes - did Queen ever rock as convincingly, as lustily, as on Tie Your Mother Down? - but it never quite escapes Opera's shadow. White Man is this album's Prophet's Song, Teo Torriate the sweeping ballad, Good Old Fashioned Lover Boy the high-camp vignette. Crucially, what Races lacks is a Bo Rhap.

But if that particular bolt of lightning refused to strike twice, the album's standout single saw Queen again draw from soul and, in particular, gospel, for Mercury's Somebody To Love, just as they had with You're My Best Friend. Soaring, inspirational, stricken and powerful on a very immediate level, its brilliance lay in the call and response interplay between Mercury and his choir of multi-tracked bandmates. What made Queen so great was not just the variety of roles they played, but how convincingly, sublimely they played them.

A Day At The Races was another appropriately grand success, but Queen were swiftly becoming aware that they were in danger of being held hostage to peoples' perceptions of what they were. Add to that the coming of punk, which killed off many of the bands they'd looked up to early in their careers, along with plenty deadwood contemporaries, and things were beginning to look a little shaky for Queen, despite their rapid ascent to the rock'n'roll firmament.

Not that sales for both the album and the accompanying world tours (including headline shows at Earl's Court) give any indication. But News Of The World, released in the winter of 1977, is the first indication that Queen are going to have to grow and struggle a little in the coming years, to maintain their crucial grip on pop's larynx. The album opens with Roger's raucous Sheer Heart Attack, an aping of and sly critique upon punk rock - all nosebleed guitars and jackhammer drums, Roger snarling "I feel so inar-inar-inarticulate!", echoing Roger Daltrey's stuttering iconoclasm in 'My Generation'. The difference is, of course, Taylor is a rich, successful rock'n'roll star gently but firmly mocking the exuberance of youth - suggesting Queen to be not entirely in tune with pop's zeitgeist.

At the same time, the album yielded two enduring Queen anthems. We Will Rock You was the stomping classic beloved of the terraces, again bizarre in its spare and lopsided structure, but undeniably brilliant. Better still was the surging We Are The Champions, a heady song of celebration buoyed up by Freddie's sense of drama and dynamics, surging from piano and vocal verses, to the earthquaking choruses bolstered by those multitracked choirs and Brian's gleaming, muscular guitar breaks. Not to mention Freddie's outstanding vocal performance, powerful without being hammy, deft but never too camp.

Queen threw themselves back into the touring/recording cycle with typically hedonistic abandon, reflected in the choice of opening single for the band's next album, recorded at the Montreux studio they subsequently purchased for their own purposes. The bands parties became legendary for their opulence and excess, while Freddie endlessly played up his sexual voracity and duality. Fittingly, **Fat Bottomed Girls / Bicycle Race**, their double-A-sided single, causes much consternation, thanks to the sexual explicitness of the former's naked-lady sleeve, and the latter's 50-naked-ladies-cycling video.

Whereas the latter was operatic art-rock Queen at their archest, the former was a sleazy little rut in the fashion of **Tie Your Mother Down**, all heaving low-end grime and loping, bad-boy breakbeats. The follow-up single, **Don't Stop Me Now**, was also prime-Queen, breakneck rock'n'roll of a good humour, Freddie and the Queen choir howling a smile-flecked paean to heedless hedonism over spitfire Brian May lead guitar. If ever a song perfectly encapsulated Freddie's joy-hungry outlook on life, this was it, while the album of whole displayed a gutsiness, a self-confidence **News Of The World** lacked somehow.

The Game, released in 1980, would be perhaps the apex of Queen's synthesis of pop wit and rock mettle. John Deacon's **Another One Bites The Dust** was a sophisticated slice of disco funk, its unforgettable opening bassline a distant cousin of Chic's 'Good Times', indeed blended into that riff on Grandmaster Flash's seminal hip-hop monster 'The Adventures Of Grandmaster Flash On The Wheels Of Steel'. It's pastiche of panache and groove was convincing enough to see Queen playlisted on urban America's 'black' radio stations for a while, and the record's success there prompted the ill-starred excursion into disco-rock that was 1982's **Hot Space** album.

Crazy Little Thing Called Love, on the other hand, was Mercury's tribute to the recently departed King Of Rock'n'Roll, Elvisly swaggering and not a little rockabilly in its shuffle. For the video, Freddie donned leathers and a mean quiff, at once referencing the bad-boy birth of rock and the modern gay disco culture Freddie was increasingly flirting with. Add the quicksilver dream-rock of title track **The Game**, the epic yet still moving power-balladry of **Save Me**, and the muscular rockout of **Dragon Attack**, and **The Game** captured Queen at their most compact and visceral. Gone is the vaudevillian whimsy of yore; Queen are no longer beholden to their past, and can take their influences where they please.

Which wasn't necessarily the best thing. 1982's **Hot Space** - released after the band's suitably stirring soundtrack to 1981's high camp sci-fi remake, **Flash** - was an attempt to capitalise on the success of **Another One Bites The Dust**, being groove-laden, synth-heavy, almost guitar-free. Singles such as **Back Chat** and **Body Language** hardly rate as classic Queen. Sales lapsed slightly as well, suggesting audiences preferred Queen rocking out, as opposed to playing with the public's perception of what they were about.

The album featured one glorious moment, however; the duet with David Bowie, **Under Pressure**. Sparse until its powerful crescendo, it's built around another nagging, simple John Deacon bass riff, and an unforgettable piano lick Vanilla Ice will steal wholesale for his regrettable 'Ice Ice Baby' single almost a decade later. As with many other Queen tunes, the true power lies in the delivery, the drama, the dynamism; the way the song builds up to the final loud explosion, Freddie singing "Can't we give love just one more chance?" as Brian kicks loud, feral guitar over the top, Bowie segueing back in and bring the tune back down to earth. Simple, yes, but deceptively so.

It's hard to deny that there was a sense around this period that Queen were taking their foot off the accelerator somewhat. Brian and Roger pursued solo projects, while all four members had money in their bank accounts to squander as they saw fit. Another Queen album wouldn't materialise until 1984, but it would be well worth waiting for.

The Works contained two of Queen's greatest hits of the 1980s. **I Want To Break Free** was more pop simplicity on the band's part; airy, clean and very compact, it was a triumph as much for its sweet, chugging melody as its brilliant video, Queen showing that, like any Englishmen, it really doesn't take much persuading to get them to dress up as ladies.

Radio Gaga also boasted a brilliant video - ironic, given that it was a celebration of a radio culture television was eating away at. Earlier that year, Freddie had contributed vocals to a soundtrack for a colourised re-release of Fritz Lang's classic 'Metropolis'; **Radio Gaga** winked towards that movie's fascistic futurism, its dystopian vision eked out in the martial handclaps that beat throughout the track. Meanwhile, subtle synths squeal and rumble throughout, while Freddie's vocals and piano carry the melody, until the cataclysmic last chorus, guitars and drums powering in with full-on anthemic muscle. Typically Queen, it's a masterpiece of build and structure, of dynamics.

Also boasting the vampish Man On The Prowl (Crazy Little Thing part two), the epic and moving It's A Hard Life, the pulverising Hammer To Fall and the melting Is This The World We Created? (the latter two dealing with environmental themes), The Works is remarkably free of filler for an album so far in the career of a world-dominating group. But Queen never hurried themselves, and it shows in the quality of their albums; and given that they were breaking box office records the world over, they had no need to skimp on the quality.

That said, 1986's A Kind Of Magic was afflicted by a certain patchiness. Perhaps this is because a number of tunes were earmarked for the soundtrack to Highlander, the Christopher Lambert and Sean Connery-starring sci-fi movie released that year (although the movie's theme of mystical immortality did provoke the stirring, bleak ballad Who Wants To Live Forever?). Perhaps it's due to Freddie's extra-curricular activities, releasing his first solo album, Mr Bad Guy, in 1985, and releasing both his cover of the Platters' classic The Great Pretender, and his Barcelona album with opera singer Montserrat Caballe in 1987. John Deacon himself had remarked a couple of years previously, "We've reached a point where we're working a little bit less as a group."

But A Kind Of Magic still delivered some classic Queen anthems. There was the overdriven rocker One Vision, itself used for the theme-tune to Lou Gosset Jr air force thriller 'Iron Eagle', and a masterpiece of the band's hard-rock sensibilities and Brian's ability to sneak pure metal guitar work into the mainstream charts somehow. And then there was the title track, another synthesis of the band's pop and rock impulses; with an almost doo-wop feel to it, conjured up by the finger-clicking intro and the multi-tracked backing vocals, the song is perhaps best remembered for Brian's impossibly-creamy guitar work and Freddie's excellent, arcing vocals.

The band toured A Kind Of Magic with typical pomp and circumstance, breaking attendance records at Wembley (where, a year before, their greatest hits performance at the Live Aid concert was universally agreed the standout of the day; and did much to improve the band's diminished post-Hot Space stocks) and playing a prestigious show at Knebworth, along with the usual hulking global domination. However, it would prove to be the band's last ever tour with Freddie. A dark cloud was gathering on the horizon.

It was May 1989 when The Miracle, Queen's thirteenth studio album, hit the shelves. Uncharacteristically heavy for a band at this stage in their career - most of their contemporaries were happy to make dull 'rock' muzak for yuppies to play on their in-car CD players - it caught Queen in another creative upswing. Was It All Worth It? wasn't as whimsical as the title suggested, being rather a deafening riff-monster, while The Miracle itself was a sweet, reflective pop song. But the big hit on the album, which also sired the melodramatic 'Scandal' and the playful Invisible Man, was I Want It All.

Trailed by a video depicting the band in wall street-esque garb - certainly a change from the leotards and tinsel of yore - it boasted a riff heavier than a tonne of bricks and some of the purest heavy metal guitar shredding from May of the band's career. With classic Queen-choir backing vocals, it seemed a twisted hymn to greed and the avarice of the 80s, and was in fact an attack on all of that ugliness.

So pleased were the band with The Miracle that they swiftly returned to the studio later that year to work on the follow-up. It's unclear whether this is because they didn't have any live performances to distract them from this endeavour, or because of Freddie's failing health. In videos for The Miracle, Freddie looked thinner than before, a layer of 'designer-stubble' disguising his gauntness; although it was kept private at this point, Freddie had contracted the HIV virus, and was dying of AIDS.

This darkness characterised the album which was to follow, Innuendo. In many ways, it was a return to the Queen sound of their 'golden age', with the title track and first single being an epic, symphonic rock tune in the vein of Bo Rhap. But Innuendo would ultimately be remembered more for two more melancholic tunes than this.

These Are The Days Of Our Lives was a strikingly lovely song, stricken with a painful poignancy atypical for Queen. This was Freddie at his most vulnerable, the mask falling to reveal a reflective, not bitter, Mercury gazing over his past achievements as he neared death. Although Freddie looked painfully ill in the video for the single, recorded in May 1991 and included as double-A side to a re-released Bohemian Rhapsody charity single that Christmas, the video still contained much of the humour that Queen had displayed throughout their career.

But it was The Show Must Go On which caught Freddie facing the inevitable in the classic Queen style, all soaring bombast and quaking, quasi-classical epicness. The song feels like a hard slog, a battle against

insurmountable odds, leavened by a sense of high drama and high camp. It's the kind of song Shirley Bassey could've made her own.

Freddie passed away on November 23rd, only a day after revealing he was suffering from AIDS. The public response to his passing was immediate and heartfelt; rock had lost one of its most flamboyant, instantly recognisable frontmen. This was a gap which wasn't ever going to be filled.

Bohemian Rhapsody was re-released that Christmas, all monies going to The Terence Higgins Trust AIDS charity. The following Spring, Queen and a host of superstar guests - including Guns'n'Roses, Metallica, Elton John and even Liza Minelli - assembled at Wembley for a tribute concert in Freddie's memory. A single from the concert, featuring George Michael fronting Queen for an exuberant run through Somebody To Love, profits from which founded the Mercury Phoenix Trust. Meanwhile, Brian and Roger pursued solo projects, sometimes joining John to play Queen numbers on special occasions (members of Queen have backed Foo Fighters, Robbie Williams, even boyband 5ive over the last decade). And Queen's legions of loyal fans were sated by collector's edition re-releases of Queen material, live albums and an exhaustive 12 CD box of Freddie's solo work (similarly impressive archival sets from Queen's unreleased backpages are expected in the coming years).

But Queen had one last album left to be released. Made In Heaven took four years to complete, and hit the shelves in 1995. It consisted of songs Freddie recorded in Montreux, during his final months, which the remaining bandmembers fleshed out after his passing. Amongst these songs - understandably sombre in tone, but still uplifting - was a song Brian had debuted at the tribute concert, Too Much Love Will Kill You. Downbeat but dramatic, it was a lovely jewel of a song; sentimental perhaps, but in a way that expressed a real, tender emotion, and communicated it to a huge audience.

Which was always Queen's way. While their name denoted a regal dictatorship, they were a band of and for the people, distilling opera and heavy rock and soul and pop and classical and campness and machismo and wit and pathos into a music without boundaries, which touched any and all open to its grandiose sweep and knowing melodrama. "Let me entertain you!" bellowed Freddie, on the song of the same name back in 1978. Throughout their career, the world did exactly that; and even beyond the grave, the fact remains the same. Doubtless, somewhere, Freddie is savouring this.

Stevie Chick has been a freelance music writer for four years, contributing to Melody Maker, NME, Kerrang!, The Times, the Evening Standard and Sleaze Nation, and is currently a contributing editor of Careless Talk Costs Lives. He lives in London and has recently completed work on his book Don't Stop Now: The Ballad Of Guided By Voices, the amazing tale of 30-something songwriter Robert Pollard's ascent from school teacher obscurity to indie-rock superstardom.

Discography:Albums

Note: This is just a partial discography, covering Queen's major releases; Queen's music has been re-released in various forms and formats over the past decade, so this discography will accommodate mainly the albums and singles released during Freddie's lifetime, along with a couple of posthumous releases.

Queen

Keep Yourself Alive
Doing Alright
Great King Rat
My Fairy King
Liar
The Night Comes Down
Modern Times Rock'n'Roll
Son & Daughter
Jesus
Seven Seas Of Rhye

Release Date: September 1973
Highest Chart Position: 24

Queen 2

Procession
Father To Son
White Queen (As It Began)
Some Day One Day
The Loser In The End
Ogre Battle
Fairy Feller's Master Stroke
Nevermore
The March Of The Black Queen
Funny How Love Is
Seven Seas Of Rhye

Release Date: April 1974
Highest Chart Position: 5

Sheer Heart Attack

Brighton Rock
Killer Queen
Tenement Funster
Flick Of The Wrist
Lily Of The Valley
Now I'm Here
In the Lap Of The Gods
Stone Cold Crazy
Dear Friends
Misfire
Bring Back That Leroy Brown
She Makes Me (Stormtrooper In Stilettos)
In The Lap Of The Gods (Reprise)

Release Date: November 1974
Highest Chart Position: 2

A Night At The Opera

Death On Two Legs
Lazing On A Sunday Afternoon
I'm In Love With My Car
You're My Best Friend
'39
Sweet Lady
Seaside Rendezvous
Prophet's Song
Love Of My Life
Good Company
Bohemian Rhapsody
God Save The Queen

Release Date: December 1975
Highest Chart Position: 1

A Day At The Races

Tie Your Mother Down
Take My Breath Away
Long Away
The Millionaire Waltz
You & I
Somebody To Love
White Man
Good Old Fashioned Loverboy
Drowse
Teo Torriate (Let Us Cling Together)

Release Date: December 1976
Highest Chart Position: 1

News Of The World

We Will Rock You
We Are The Champions
Sheer Heart Attack
All Dead, All Dead
Spread Your Wings
Fight From The Inside
Get Down, Make Love
Sleeping On The Sidewalk
Who Needs You?
It's Late
My Melancholy Blues
We Will Rock You

Release Date: November 1977
Highest Chart Position: 4

Jazz

Mustafa
Fat Bottomed Girls
Jealousy
Bicycle Race
If You Can't Beat Them
Let Me Entertain You
Dead On Time
In Only Seven Days
Dreamer's Ball
Fun It
Leaving Home Ain't Easy
Don't Stop Me Now
More Of That Jazz

Release Date: November 1978
Highest Chart Position: 2

Live Killers

We Will Rock You
Let Me Entertain You
Death On Two Legs
Killer Queen
Bicycle Race
I'm In Love With My Car
Get Down, Make Love
You're My Best Friend
Now I'm Here
Dreamer's Ball
Love Of My Life
'39
Keep Yourself Alive
Don't Stop Me Now
Spread Your Wings
Brighton Rock
Bohemian Rhapsody
Tie Your Mother Down
Sheer Heart Attack
We Will Rock You
We Are The Champions
God Save The Queen

Release Date: June 1979
Highest Chart Position: 3

Discography:Albums

The Game

Play The Game
Dragon Attack
Another One Bites The Dust
Need Your Loving Tonight
Crazy Little Thing Called Love
Rock It (Prime Jive)
Don't Try Suicide
Sail Away Sweet Sister
Coming Soon
Save Me

Release Date: June 1980
Highest Chart Position: 1

Flash Gordon

Flash's Theme
In The Space Capsule (Love Theme)
Ming's Theme
The Ring
Football Fight
In the Death Cell
Execution Of Flash
The Kiss
Arboria
Escape From The Swamp
Flash To The Rescue
Vultan's Theme
Battle Theme
The Wedding March
The Marriage Of Dale And Ming
Crash Dive On Mingo City
Flash's Theme Reprise
The Hero
Flash's Theme

Release Date: January 1981
Highest Chart Position: 10

Hot Space

Staying Power
Dancer
Backchat
Body Language
Action This Day
Put Out This Fire
Life Is Real (Song For Lennon)
Calling All Girls
Las Parablas De Amor (The Words Of Love)
Cool Cat
Under Pressure

Release Date: May 1982
Highest Chart Position: 4

The Works

Radio Gaga
Tear It Up
It's A Hard Life
Man On The Prowl
Machines (Back To Humans)
I Want To Break Free
Keep Passing The Open Windows
Hammer To Fall
Is This The World We Created?

Release Date: February 1984
Highest Chart Position: 2

A Kind Of Magic

One Vision
A Kind Of Magic
One Year Of Love
Pain Is So Close To Pleasure
Friends Will Be Friends
Who Wants To Live Forever?
Gimme The Prize
Don't Lose Your Head
Princes Of The Universe

Release Date: June 1986
Highest Chart Position: 1

Live Magic

One Vision
Tie Your Mother Down
Seven Seas Of Rhye
A Kind Of Magic
Under Pressure
Another One Bites The Dust
I Want To Break Free
Is This The World We Created?
Bohemian Rhapsody
Hammer To Fall
Radio Gaga
We Will Rock You
Friends Will Be Friends
We Are The Champions
God Save The Queen

Release Date: 1986
Highest Chart Position: 3

The Miracle

The Party
Khashoggi's Ship
The Miracle
I Want It All
Invisible Man
Breakthru
Rain Must Fall
Scandal
My Baby Does Me
Was It All Worth It?
Hang On In There
Chinese Torture

Release Date: June 1989
Highest Chart Position: 1

Innuendo

Innuendo
I'm Going Slightly Mad
Headlong
I Can't Live With You
Don't Try So Hard
Ride The Wild Wind
All God's People
These Are The Days Of Our Lives
Delilah
The Hitman
Bijou
The Show Must Go On

Release Date: February 1991
Highest Chart Position: 1

Made In Heaven

It's A Beautiful Day
Made In Heaven
Let Me Live
Mother Love
My Life Has Been Saved
I Was Born To Love You
Heaven For Everyone
Too Much Love Will Kill You
You Don't Fool Me
A Winter's Tale
It's A Beautiful Day (Reprise)
Yeah

Release Date: November 1995
Highest Chart Position: 1

Discography:Singles

Keep Yourself Alive
Release Date: July 1973
Highest Chart Position: N/A

Seven Seas Of Rhye
Release Date: February 1974
Highest Chart Position: 10

Killer Queen
Release Date: October 1974
Highest Chart Position: 2

Now I'm Here
Release Date: January 1975
Highest Chart Position: 11

Bohemian Rhapsody
Release Date: October 1975
Highest Chart Position: 1

You're My Best Friend
Release Date: May 1976
Highest Chart Position: 7

Somebody To Love
Release Date: November 1976
Highest Chart Position: 2

Tie Your Mother Down
Release Date: March 1977
Highest Chart Position: 31

Queen's First Ep
(Good Old Fashioned Loverboy)
Release Date: May 1977
Highest Chart Position: 17

We Are The Champions
Release Date: October 1977
Highest Chart Position: 2

Spread Your Wings
Release Date: February 1978
Highest Chart Position: 34

Bicycle Race /
Fat Bottomed Girls
Release Date: October 1978
Highest Chart Position: 11

Don't Stop Me Now
Release Date: January 1979
Highest Chart Position: 9

Love Of My Life
Release Date: June 1979
Highest Chart Position: 63

Crazy Little Thing Called Love
Release Date: October 1979
Highest Chart Position: 2

Save Me
Release Date: January 1980
Highest Chart Position: 11

Play The Game
Release Date: May 1980
Highest Chart Position: 14

Another One Bites The Dust
Release Date: August 1980
Highest Chart Position: 7

Flash!
Release Date: November 1980
Highest Chart Position: 10

Under Pressure
Release Date: October 1981
Highest Chart Position: 1

Body Language
Release Date: April 1982
Highest Chart Position: 25

Las Parablas De Amor
Release Date: June 1982
Highest Chart Position: 25

Backchat
Release Date: August 1982
Highest Chart Position: 40

Radio Gaga
Release Date: January 1984
Highest Chart Position: 2

I Want To Break Free
Release Date: April 1984
Highest Chart Position: 3

It's A Hard Life
Release Date: July 1984
Highest Chart Position: 6

Hammer To Fall
Release Date: September 1984
Highest Chart Position: 8

Thank God It's Christmas
Release Date: November 1984
Highest Chart Position: 21

One Vision
Release Date: November 1985
Highest Chart Position: 7

A Kind Of Magic
Release Date: March 1986
Highest Chart Position: 3

Friends Will Be Friends
Release Date: June 1986
Highest Chart Position: 14

Who Wants To Live Forever?
Release Date: September 1986
Highest Chart Position: 24

I Want It All
Release Date: May 1989
Highest Chart Position: 3

Breakthru
Release Date: June 1989
Highest Chart Position: 7

The Invisible Man
Release Date: August 1989
Highest Chart Position: 12

Scandal
Release Date: October 1989
Highest Chart Position: 25

The Miracle
Release Date: November 1989
Highest Chart Position: 21

Innuendo
Release Date: January 1991
Highest Chart Position: 1

I'm Going Slightly Mad
Release Date: March 1991
Highest Chart Position: 22

Headlong
Release Date: May 1991
Highest Chart Position: 14

The Show Must Go On
Release Date: October 1991
Highest Chart Position: 16

Bohemian Rhapsody /
These Are The Days Of Our Lives
Release Date: December 1991
Highest Chart Position: 1

Heaven For Everyone
Release Date: November 1995
Highest Chart Position: 2

A Winter's Tale
Release Date: December 1995
Highest Chart Position: 6

Too Much Love Will Kill You
Release Date: March 1996
Highest Chart Position: 15

Let Me Live
Release Date: June 1996
Highest Chart Position: 9

Killer Queen

Words and Music by
FREDDIE MERCURY

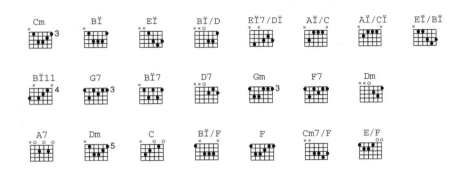

Verse 1

Medium Rock

$\frac{4}{4}$ |Cm |B♭ |

She keeps Moet and Chandon in her pretty cabinet,

Cm |B♭ |

'Let them eat cake,' she says, just like Marie Antoinette. A

B♭/D |E♭/D♭ A♭/C |

built in remedy for Krushchev and Kennedy, and

A♭m/C♭ E♭/B♭ |B♭11 |$\frac{2}{4}$ |

any time an invitation you can decline.

$\frac{4}{4}$ G7 Cm |

Caviar and cigarettes,

B♭7 E♭ |D7 Gm F7 |

well versed in etiquette, extr'ordinarily nice. She's a

Chorus 1

B♭ Dm/A |Gm Dm |Gm A7 Dm |

Killer Queen, gunpowder, gelatine, dynamite with a laser beam,

$\frac{3}{4}$ G7 |$\frac{3}{8}$ C B♭ |$\frac{3}{4}$ |

guaranteed to blow your mind, anytime, ooh.

A7 Dm |G7 Cm |

Recommended at the price, insatiable an appetite

C B♭ |F B♭/F F7 |B♭/F |F B♭ F7 |B♭/F |

wanna try. To a-

Verse 2

Cm | B♭ |
void complications, she never kept the same address,

Cm | B♭ |
In conversation she spoke just like a baroness.

                B♭/D | E♭/D♭   A♭/C |
Met a man from China, went down to Geisha Minah,

A♭m/C♭   E♭/B♭ | B♭11 | $\frac{2}{4}$ |
then again incidentally if you're that way inclined. Perfume came

$\frac{4}{4}$ G7   Cm |
   nat'rally from Paris, for

B♭7   E♭ | D7   Gm   F7 |
cars she couldn't care less, fastidious and precise. She's a

Chorus 2

B♭   Dm/A | Gm   Dm | Gm   A7   Dm |
Killer Queen, gunpowder, gelatine, dynamite with a laser beam,

$\frac{3}{4}$ G7 | $\frac{3}{8}$ C   B♭ | $\frac{3}{4}$ |
  guaranteed to blow your   mind,   anytime, ooh.

    A   Dm   A   Dm   G7   Cm   G7   Cm
| /   /   /   / | /   /   /   / | /   /   /   / | /   /   /   / |

Interlude

    Cm7/F   F   E/F   F   Cm
$\frac{4}{4}$ | /   /   /   / | /   /   /   / | /   /   /   /   / | /   /   /   / |

    B♭   Cm   B♭   E♭   B♭/D
| /   /   /   / | /   /   /   / | /   /   /   / | /   /   /   / |

    E♭7/D♭   A♭/ C   A♭m/C♭   E♭/B♭   B♭7
| /   /   /   / | / /   /   / | /   /   /   / | $\frac{2}{4}$ /   / |

$\frac{4}{4}$ E♭/B♭ | B♭7 |
      Drop of a

G7   Cm | G7   Cm |
hat she's as willing as, playful as a pussycat, then

B♭   E♭ | B♭   E♭ |
momentarily out of action, temporarily out of gas; to

D7   Gm   F | B♭   F | B♭m   F | $\frac{2}{4}$ |
absolutely drive you wild,   wild.   She's a

Chorus 3 $\frac{4}{4}$ B♭   Dm/A | Gm   Dm | Gm   A⁷ Dm |
Killer Queen, gunpowder, gelatine, dynamite with a laser beam,

$\frac{3}{4}$ G⁷ | $\frac{3}{8}$ C   B♭ | $\frac{3}{4}$ |
guaranteed to blow your   mind,   anytime, ooh.

$\frac{4}{4}$ A⁷   Dm | G⁷   Cm |
Recommended at the price, insatiable an appetite

C   B♭ |
what a drag.

F   B♭/F F⁷   B♭/F
| / / /   / | / / / / |

F   B♭/F F⁷   B♭/F   *(Last 2 bars*
| / / /   / | / / / / | / / / / | / / / / | *repeat for fade)*

Bohemian Rhapsody

Words and Music by
FREDDIE MERCURY

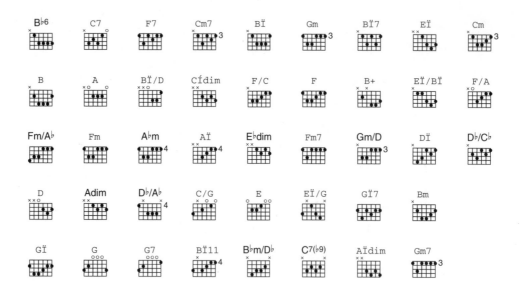

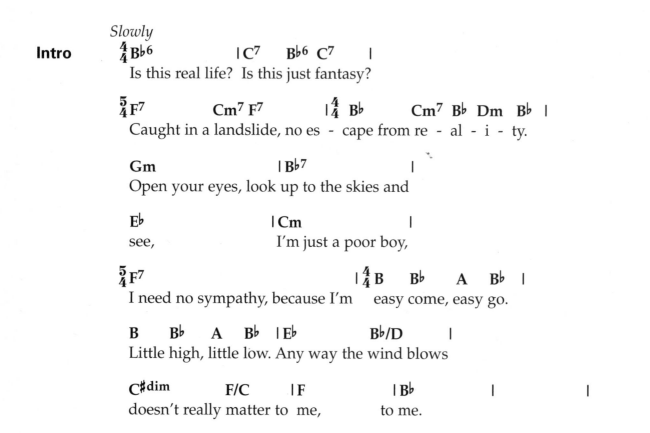

Slowly

Intro $\frac{4}{4}$ B♭6 | C7   B♭6   C7 |

Is this real life? Is this just fantasy?

$\frac{5}{4}$ F7   Cm7 F7 | $\frac{4}{4}$ B♭   Cm7 B♭ Dm B♭ |

Caught in a landslide, no es - cape from re - al - i - ty.

Gm | B♭7 |

Open your eyes, look up to the skies and

E♭ | Cm |

see,   I'm just a poor boy,

$\frac{5}{4}$ F7 | $\frac{4}{4}$ B   B♭   A   B♭ |

I need no sympathy, because I'm   easy come, easy go.

B   B♭   A   B♭ | E♭   B♭/D |

Little high, little low. Any way the wind blows

C♯dim   F/C | F | B♭ | |

doesn't really matter to me,   to me.

Verse 1

Bb |Gm |
Mama just killed a man, put a

Cm |F |
gun against his head, pulled my trigger, now he's dead.

Bb |Gm |
Mama, life had just begun, but

Cm⁷   B+   Eb/Bb |F/A   Fm/Ab |
now I've gone and thrown it all   away.

Eb   Bb/D |Cm |
Mama, ooh,   didn't

Fm |Bb |
mean to make you cry. If I'm not back again this time to-

Eb   Bb/D |Cm Abm |
morrow, carry on, carry on as if nothing really

Eb   Ab   Eb |²⁄₄ Ebdim   Fm⁷ |
matters.

Bb
⁴⁄₄| / / / / | / / / / |

Verse 2

Bb |Gm |
Too late, my time has come. Sends

Cm |F |
shivers down my spine, body's aching all the time.

Bb |Gm |
Goodbye ev'rybody, I've got to go, gotta

Cm⁷   B+   Eb/Bb |F/A   Fm⁷Ab |
leave you all behind and face the truth.

Eb   Bb/D |Cm |
Mama,   ooh,

Fm |Bb |
I don't want to die, I sometimes wish I'd never been born at

Eb   Bb/D |Cm |
all.

Fm Bb7 Eb   Gm/D

| / / / / | / / / / |

Cm   Fm   Db Db/Cb Bbm

| / / / / | / / / / | / / /   / |

Interlude   **A** *(double time)*

| / / / / | / / / / |

D   A   Adim A |D A   Adim A |
I   see a little silhouetto of a   man, Scara-

D   A D   A |Adim A D A |
mouche, Scaramouche, will you do the Fandango.

Db   Ab |C/G   E |
Chorus Thunderbolt and lightning, very, very fright'ning

A N.C. | |
me. *Gallileo.* Gallileo. *Gallileo.* Galli-

             |**2/4** |**4/4** |
leo, Gallileo, Figaro Magnifico

B Bb A Bb |B Bb   A Bb |
Solo I'm just a poor boy and nobody loves me.

Ab Eb   Ebdim Eb |Ab   Eb   Ebdim Eb |
Chorus He's just a poor   boy from a poor famil - y.

Ab   Eb/G |F   Bb |Ab Eb/G F#dim Fm7 |
Spare him his life from this monstrosity.

B Bb A Bb |B   Bb   A Bb |
Solo Easy come, easy go,   will you let me go. Bis-

Eb   Bb |Eb |
millah! *Chorus* No, we will not let you go. *Let him go!*

            Bb |Eb |
Bismillah! We will not let you go. *Let him go!*

           Bb | |
Bismillah! We will not let you go. *Let me go!*

                     | |
Will not let you go. *Let me go.* Will not let you go. *Let me go.*

Gb7 |Bm A D Db |
Ah.   No, no, no, no,

G♭　B♭　E♭　N.C.　　|E♭　　　　　　|
no,　no, no.　*Oh mama mia, mama mia.* Mama

B♭　　　　　　　|E♭　A♭　　|
mia, let me go. Be-elzebub has a

D　　　Gm　　|B♭　　　　　|
devil put aside for me, for

　　　　|　　　　|　　　　|
me, for me.

　　E♭
|／／／／|／／／／|／／／／|／／／／|

B♭⁷　　E♭/B♭　　|B♭　　E♭　　|B♭　　|²₄ D♭　　|
So you think you can stone me and spit in my eye.

⁴₄ B♭⁷　E♭/B♭　　|B♭　　E♭　　|A♭　　|Fm　　|
So you think you can love me and leave me to die.　　Oh,

B♭　　　　|Fm　　　|B♭　　　|
baby,　　　can't do this to me, baby.

Fm⁷　　B♭ |Fm⁷　　B♭　　|
Just gotta get out,　just gotta get right outta here.

　　E♭　　　　　　B♭⁷ *(slowing down and getting quieter)*
|／／／／|／／／／|／／／／|／／／／|

Slowly

Coda　　E♭　B♭　Cm　G Cm　G⁷ Cm B♭⁷ E♭　D　Gm
|／／／／|／／／／|／／／／|／／／／|

A♭　　　　E♭　|Cm　　Gm　　|
　　　Nothing really matters,

Cm　　Gm　　|Cm　　A♭m　|
anyone can see,　　nothing really matters,

B♭¹¹　　　　　|E♭　　A♭/E♭　|
nothing really matters to me.

　　E♭　E♭dim B♭/D B♭m/D♭
|／／／／|／／／／|

　　C⁷　C7-9　C⁷　F *(slowing down and getting quieter)*
|／／／／|／／／／|

B♭　F　　A♭dim Gm⁷　　|F　　　　‖
Any way the wind　blows.

19

Crazy Little Thing Called Love

Words and Music by
FREDDIE MERCURY

D   G   C

B♭   E   A

Medium shuffle beat

Intro   4/4 D | | | |

This thing

Verse 1

D | |G |C   G |
called love   I just   can't handle it, this thing

D | |G |C   G |
called love   I must   get round to it, I ain't

D |B♭   C |D | |
ready.   Crazy little thing called love.   This thing

Verse 2

D | |
This thing called love *called love* it cries

G |C   G |
like a baby in a cradle all night, it swings

D | |
woo woo   it jives *woo woo*   it

G |C   G |
shakes all over like a jelly fish,   I kinda

D |B♭   C |
like it.   Crazy little thing called love.

D | |
There goes my

Chorus 1

G | |C |G |
baby,   she knows how to rock'n'roll. She drives me

B♭ | |
crazy   she gives me

```
E          A          |F                                    |
hot and cold fever, then she leaves me in a cool, cool sweat.

N.C.                |              |E            |A              |
                                                  I gotta be cool
```

Verse 3
```
            D          |              |G            |C          G        |
              relax,      get hip,            get on my tracks, take a

            D                |                    |
            backseat, hitch-hike,               and

            G                    |C        G        |
            take a long ride on my motorbike until I'm

            D        |Bb        C            |D        |              |
            ready.      Crazy little thing called love.      There goes my
```

Chorus 2   *(as Chorus 1)*

Verse 4
```
            D          |              |G            |C          G        |
              relax,      get hip,            get on my tracks, take a

            D                |                    |
            backseat, hitch-hike,               and

            G                    |C        G        |
            take a long ride on my motorbike until I'm

            D                |Bb        C            |
            ready. *Ready Freddie.* Crazy little thing called love.

            D              |                    |
                                    This thing
```

Verse 5
```
            D          |              |G            |C        G        |
            called love    I just              can't handle it, this thing

            D          |              |G            |C        G        |
            called love    I must              get round to it, I ain't

            D        |Bb        C            |D              |
            ready.      Crazy little thing called love.

            Bb        C              |D                |*(Repeat last two bars*
            Crazy little thing called love,                  *till fade)*
```
```
                                                                          21
```

Don't Stop Me Now

Words and Music by
FREDDIE MERCURY

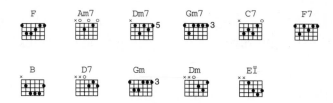

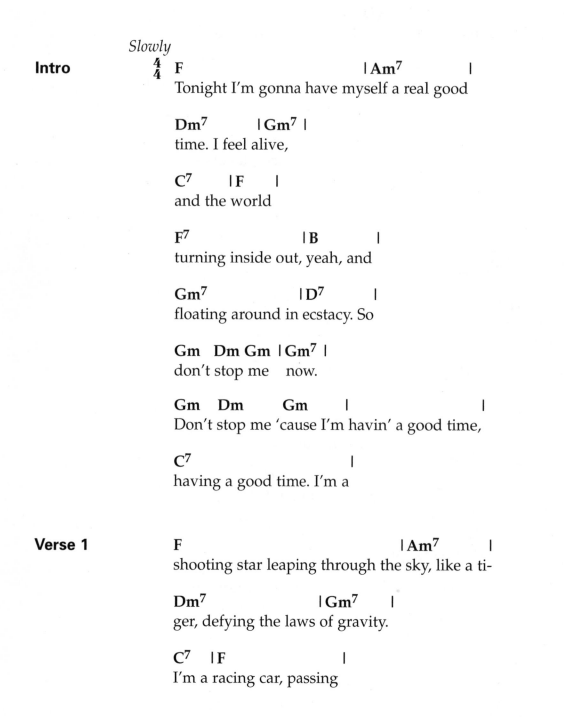

Slowly

Intro $\frac{4}{4}$ **F**   **|Am⁷**   **|**
Tonight I'm gonna have myself a real good

Dm⁷   **|Gm⁷ |**
time. I feel alive,

C⁷   **|F**   **|**
and the world

F⁷   **|B**   **|**
turning inside out, yeah, and

Gm⁷   **|D⁷**   **|**
floating around in ecstacy. So

Gm   **Dm Gm** **|Gm⁷ |**
don't stop me   now.

Gm   **Dm**   **Gm**   **|**   **|**
Don't stop me 'cause I'm havin' a good time,

C⁷   **|**
having a good time. I'm a

Verse 1   **F**   **|Am⁷**   **|**
shooting star leaping through the sky, like a ti-

Dm⁷   **|Gm⁷**   **|**
ger, defying the laws of gravity.

C⁷   **|F**   **|**
I'm a racing car, passing

Am   **|Dm** |
by like Lady Godiva. I'm gonna

Gm⁷   **|C⁷** |
go, go, go. There's no stoppin'

F   **|F⁷** |
me. I'm burnin' through the

B♭   **|Gm⁷** |
sky, yeah. Two hundred degrees, that's why they

D⁷   **|Gm** |
call me Mister Fahrenheit. I'm

D⁷   **|Gm⁷** |
trav'ling at the speed of light. I wanna make a

B♭   **|C** |
supersonic man out of you.

Chorus
    F   **Gm F** **|Dm** |
Don't stop me now, I'm havin' such a

Gm⁷   **|C⁷** |
good time, I'm havin' a ball.

F   **Gm F** **|Dm** |
Don't stop me now, if you wanna have a

Gm⁷   **|C⁷** |
good time, just give me a call.

Gm   **Dm Gm⁷** | |
Don't stop me now.

Gm   **Dm Gm⁷** | |
Don't stop me now. I

C   **|E♭** | |
don't want to stop at all.   I'm a

Verse 2
    F   **|Am⁷** |
rocket ship on my way to Mars, on a col-

Dm⁷   **|Gm⁷** |
lision course. I am a satellite I'm

C⁷   **| F**   **|**
out of control, I am a sex machine, ready to re-

Am   **| Dm**   **|**
load, like an atom bomb, about to

Gm⁷   **| C⁷**   **|**
oh, oh, oh, oh , oh, ex-

F   **| F⁷**   **|**
plode. I'm burnin' through the

B♭   **| Gm⁷**   **|**
sky, yeah. Two hundred degrees, that's why they

D⁷   **| Gm |**
call me Mister Fahrenheit. I'm

D⁷   **| Gm**   **|**
trav'ling at the speed of light. I wanna make a

B♭   **| N.C. |**
supersonic woman of you.

Interlude   **|**   **|**
Don't stop me, don't stop me, don't

           | **B♭ |**
stop me. Don't stop me, don't stop me, ooh,

F   C   N.C. | **|**
ooh, ooh, don't stop me, have a

           | **|**   **|**
good time, good time. Don't stop me, don't stop me. *(spoken) Ah!*

Verse 3
(Instrumental)

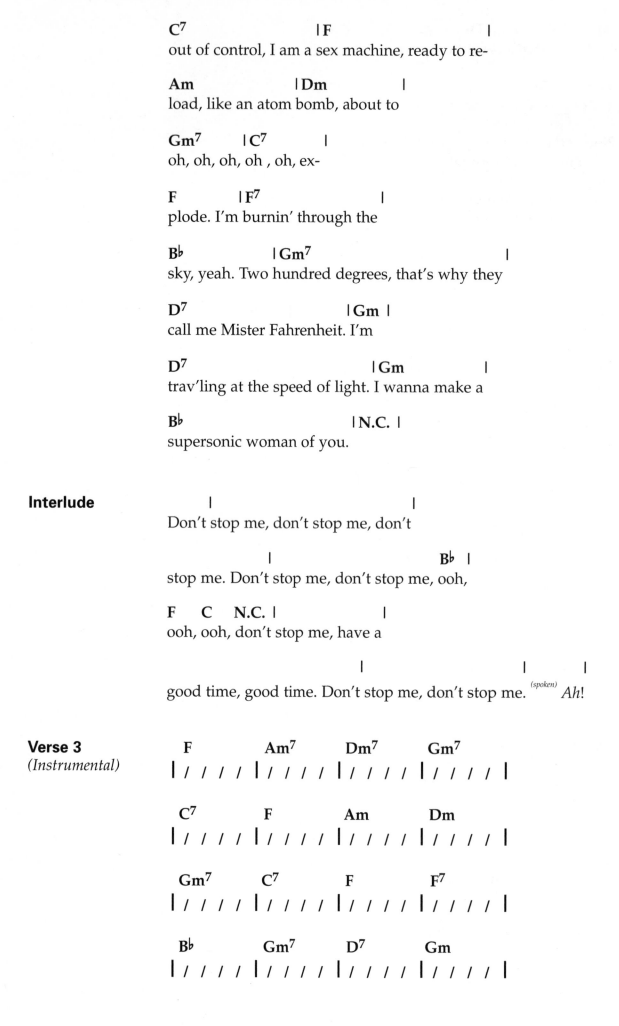

$$D^7 \quad\quad Gm^7 \quad\quad B\flat \quad\quad C$$

| / / / / | / / / / | / / / / | / / / / |

Chorus

F   Gm   F |Dm |
Don't stop me now, I'm havin' such a

Gm⁷ |C⁷ |
good time, I'm havin' a ball.

F   Gm   F |Dm |
Don't stop me now, if you wanna have a

Gm⁷ |C⁷ |
good time, just give me a call.

Gm   Dm   Gm⁷ | |
Don't stop me now.

Gm   Dm   Gm⁷ | |
Don't stop me now.

C |E♭ |
Don't want to stop at all.

Coda
(fade out)

La la la la la (etc.) *(Chords as Introduction)*

Fat Bottomed Girls

Words and Music by
BRIAN MAY

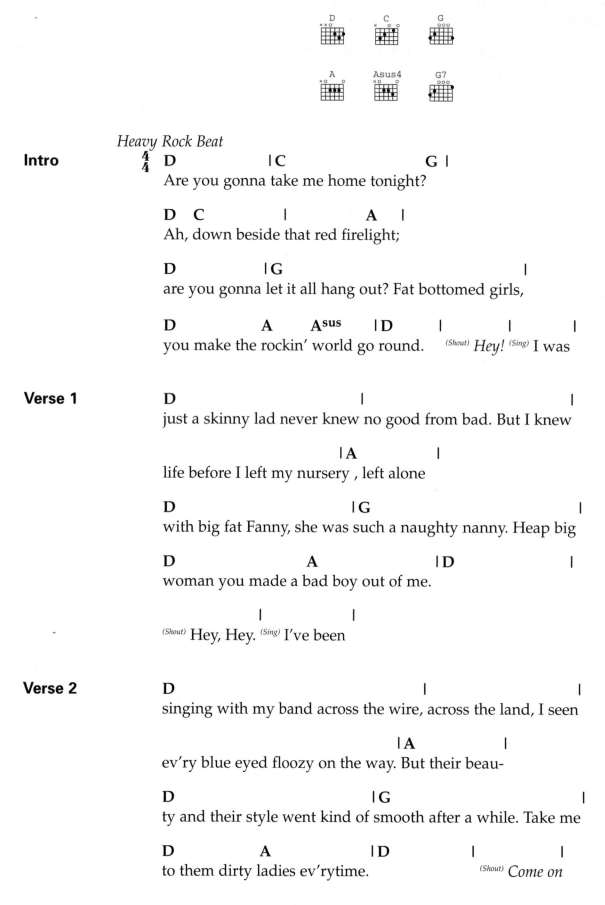

Intro

Heavy Rock Beat

4/4 **D** |**C**   **G** |
Are you gonna take me home tonight?

D **C** | **A** |
Ah, down beside that red firelight;

D |**G** |
are you gonna let it all hang out? Fat bottomed girls,

D   **A**   **A**sus |**D** | | |
you make the rockin' world go round.   *(Shout)* *Hey!* *(Sing)* I was

Verse 1

D | |
just a skinny lad never knew no good from bad. But I knew

|**A** |
life before I left my nursery , left alone

D |**G** |
with big fat Fanny, she was such a naughty nanny. Heap big

D   **A** |**D** |
woman you made a bad boy out of me.

| |
(Shout) Hey, Hey. *(Sing)* I've been

Verse 2

D | |
singing with my band across the wire, across the land, I seen

|**A** |
ev'ry blue eyed floozy on the way. But their beau-

D |**G** |
ty and their style went kind of smooth after a while. Take me

D   **A** |**D** | |
to them dirty ladies ev'rytime.   *(Shout)* *Come on*

Chorus 1

                                 |C   G |
(Sing)   Oh, won't you take me home tonight?

D |C   A |
Oh, down beside your red firelight.

D |G |
Oh and you give it all you got, fat bottomed girls

D   A |D   G |
You make the rockin' world go 'round. Fat bottomed girls

D   A |D |
you make the rockin' world go 'round.

  G G⁷ D   A   D   G   D
| / / / / | / / / / | / / / / |

A D G |$\frac{2}{4}$ |
(Shout)   Hey, listen here.*(Sing)* Now your

Verse 3 $\frac{4}{4}$ D | |
mortgages and homes, and the stiffness in your bones. Ain't no

                          |A |
beauty queens in this locality. *(I tell you)* Oh, but I

D |G |
still get my pleasure still got my greatest treasure. Heap big

D   A |
woman you gonna make a big man out of me.

D | |
(Shout) Now get this.

Chorus 2

                           |C   G |
(Sing) Oh, you gonna take me home tonight. *(please)*

D |C   A |
Oh, down beside your red firelight.

D |G |
Oh, you gonna let it all hang out, fat bottomed girls

D   A |D   G |
you make the rockin' world go 'round. Fat bottomed girls

D   A |D |
you make the rockin' world go 'round.

                            |

(Shout) Get on your bikes and ride.

Coda *(Repeat*
   till fade) | |

          (From 3rd time ad lib) Fat bottomed girls

I Want To Break Free

Words and Music by
JOHN DEACON

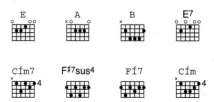

Intro ♩ = 108
 4/4 E | | | |
                                                                    I want to break

Verse 1 | | | |
         free,   I want to break free.   I want to break

                                   | | A |
         free from your lies, you're so self satisfied, I don't need you.

                            | E | |
         I've got to break free,   God

Chorus 1   B | A | E | |
         knows,   God knows I want to break free.   I've fallen in

Verse 2 | |
         love,   I've fallen in

                                   | |
         love for the first time and this time I know it's for

         A | | E | |
         real.   I've fallen in love.   Yeah!   God

Chorus 2   B | A | E | E⁷ |
         knows,   God knows I've fallen in love.   It's

Interlude   B | A |
strange, but it's true,   hey,

                 B | A |
I can't get over the way you love me like you do, but I

                 C#m^7 | F#sus4   F#^{7} |
have to be sure when I walk out that door.

                 A   B | C#m | A   B | C#m |
Oh how I want to be free baby,   oh how I want to be free,   oh

                 A   B | E | |
how I want to break free.

    | / / / / | / / / / | / / / / | / / / / |

      A   E
    | / / / / | / / / / | / / / / | / / / / |

                 B | A | E | |
                                                          But life still goes

Verse 3 | |
          on,   I can't get used to

                                             | |
living without, living without, living without you by my side.

                 A | | E | |
                        I don't want to live alone.   Hey!   God

Coda   B | A | E | |
              knows.   Got to make it on my own,   so baby can't you

              B | A | E | |
              see,   I've got to break free?   I've got to break

              E | | | | *(repeat last*
              free,   I want to break free.   Yeah!   *4 bars*
                                                       ad lib to fade)

I Want It All

Words and Music by
FREDDIE MERCURY, BRIAN MAY, ROGER TAYLOR AND JOHN DEACON

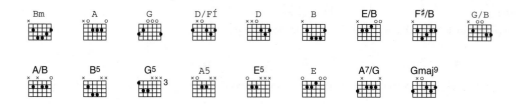

♩ = 92

Intro   4/4 Bm A Bm |G D/F♯ G |A G A |Bm   A |
                                                Adventure

Verse 1   Bm |G   D/F♯ G |
              seeker on an empty street,   just an alley

              A G A |Bm   A |
              creeper, light on his feet.   A young fighter

              Bm |G   D/F♯   G |
              screaming with no time for doubt,   with the pain and

              A G A |Bm   A |
              anger can't see a way out.   It ain't much I'm

              D   G   A | G   A |
              asking, I heard him say, gotta find me a

                          |G |
              future, move out of my way. I want it

Chorus 1   Bm A Bm |G D/F♯ G |
               all,   I want it all,   I want it

               A G A |Bm   A |
               all,   and I want it now.   I want it

               Bm A Bm |G D/F♯ G |
               all,   I want it all,   I want it

               A G A |Bm   A |
               all,   and I want it now.   Listen all you peo-

Verse 2
```
Bm                        |G                    |
```
ple, come gather round. I gotta get me a

```
A                         |Bm              A  |
```
game plan, gotta shake you to the ground. Just

```
Bm                        |G                    |
```
give me, oh, what I know is mine, people do you

```
A          |Bm          A              |
```
hear me? Just give me the sign. It ain't much I'm

```
D      G        A      |G      A  |
```
asking, if you want the truth, here's to the

```
D          A      |G                    |
```
future for the dreams of youth. (Hey!) I want it

Chorus 2
```
Bm  A  Bm      |G  D/F♯  G              ·|
```
all,   I want it all,   (Hey!) I want it

```
A  G  A              |Bm    A        |
```
all   and I want it now.   *I want it*

```
Bm  A   Bm                |G  D/F♯ G          |
```
all,   Yes! I want it all. *I want it all,*   Yeah! *I want it*

```
A  G  A                |
```
all   and I want it

Interlude
```
B                      |E/B          F♯/B          |
```
now.

```
B                               |E/B              F♯/B        |
```
I'm a man with a one track mind, so much to do in one lifetime.

```
B                           |E/B              F♯/B          |
```
Not a man for compromise and wheres and whys and living lies. *So I'm*

```
G/B                            |A/B            |          |
```
living it all, yes I'm living it all, *and I'm giving it all,* giving it all.

♩ = 140
```
   B⁵         G⁵         A⁵         E⁵
| /  /  /  / | /  /  /  / | /  /  /  / | /  /  /  / |

   B⁵         G⁵         A⁵         E⁵
| /  /  /  / | /  /  /  / | /  /  /  / | /  /  /  / |
```

Bm   **G**   **A**   **E**

| / / / / | / / / / | / / / / | / / / / |

Bm   **G**   **A**   **G**   **D/F♯**   **G**   **D/F♯**

| / / / / | / / / / | / / / / | /   /   /   / |

♩ = 92

A⁷/G |**D/F♯**   **G**   **A** |
It ain't much I'm asking if you want the truth.

G   **A** | |**G**   **A** |
Here's to the future, hear the cry of youth. *I want it*

Coda   **Bm** |**G** |**A** |**Bm**   **A** |
all I want it all, I want it all, and I want it now.   *I want it*

Bm   **A**   **Bm** |**G**   **D/F♯**   **G** |
all,   Yeah! *I want it all,*   *I want it*

A   **G**   **A** |**Bm**   **A** |
all,   *and I want it now.* Oh

   Bm   **A**   **Bm**   **G**   **D/F♯**   **G**

| / / / / / | / / /   / |

A   **G**   **A** |**Bm**   **A**   **G**ᵐᵃʲ⁹ |
    And I want it now.

| | ‖
I want it,   *I want it.*

A Kind Of Magic

Words and Music by
ROGER TAYLOR

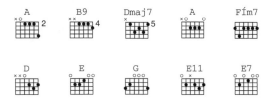

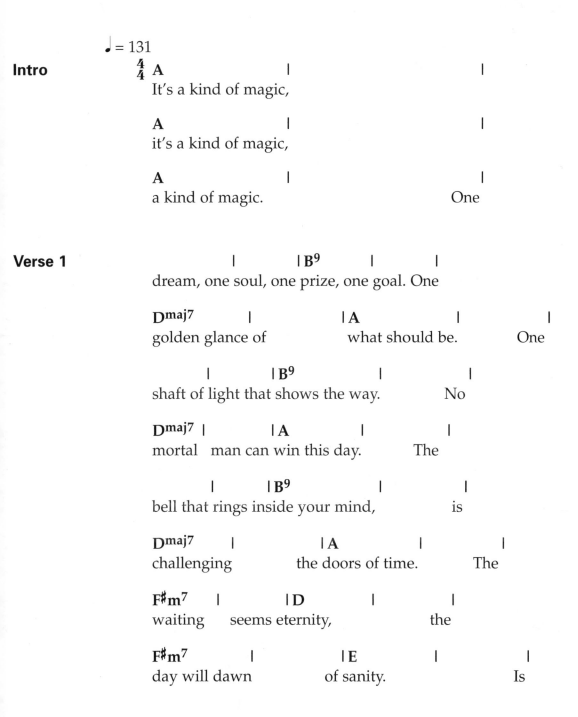

Chorus 1

```
D          |        | A        |        |
this    a kind   of magic?      There
```

```
D          |        | A        |        |
can          be only one.          This
```

```
E        | G      | D            |              | E      |      |
rage that lasts   a thousand years  will soon be gone,       this
```

Verse 2

```
              |       | B⁹      |        |
flame, that burns inside of me. I'm
```

```
D^maj7 |        | A        |        |
hearing     secret harmonies.       The
```

```
              |       | B⁹      |        |
bell that rings    inside your mind,          is
```

```
D^maj7      |             | A        |        |
challenging          the doors of time.
```

Chorus 2

```
D            |            | A        |                    |
                                  It's a kind of magic.
```

```
D            |            | A        |                    |
                                  It's a kind of magic.
```

```
   D                   A
| / / / / | / / / / | / / / / | / / / / |
```

```
D            |            | A        |                    |
                                                      This
```

```
E            | G         | D        |        |
rage       that lasts    a thousand years will soon be,
```

```
E¹¹                      | E              |
will soon be, will soon be, done.       This
```

Chorus 3

```
D          |        | A      |      |
is      a kind   of magic.    There
```

```
D          |        | A      |      |
can     be only     one.      This
```

E |G |D | |
rage that lasts   a thousand years will soon be

E | |
done.

Coda |D | |A | |
It's a kind of magic,

|D | |A | | |
it's a kind of magic, magic, magic.

D   A
| / / / / | / / / / | / / / / | / / / / |

(Last 4 bars repeat ad lib. to fade)

Radio Ga-Ga

Words and Music by
ROGER TAYLOR

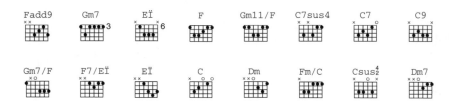

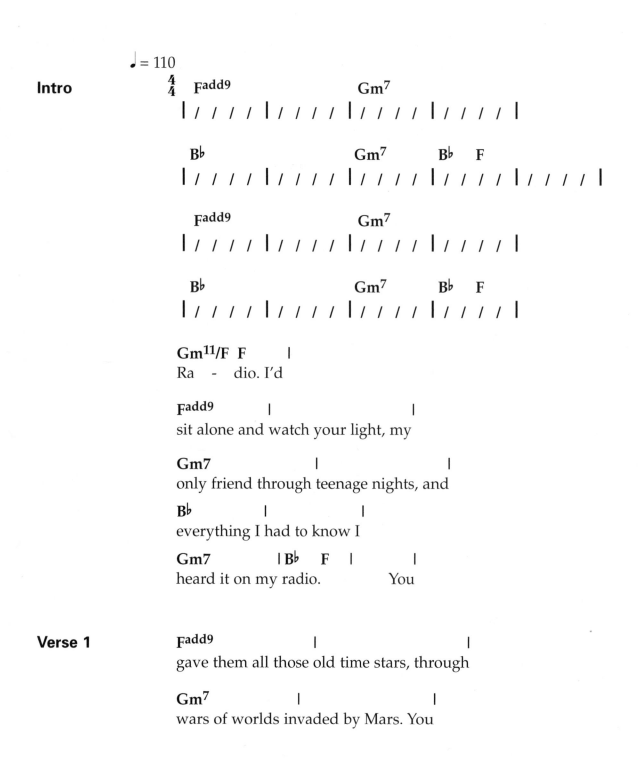

♩ = 110

Intro $\frac{4}{4}$ **Fadd9**   **Gm⁷**

| / / / / | / / / / | / / / / | / / / / |

B♭   **Gm⁷**   **B♭   F**

| / / / / | / / / / | / / / / | / / / / | / / / / |

Fadd9   **Gm⁷**

| / / / / | / / / / | / / / / | / / / / |

B♭   **Gm⁷**   **B♭   F**

| / / / / | / / / / | / / / / | / / / / |

Gm¹¹/F   F |
Ra - dio. I'd

Fadd9 | |
sit alone and watch your light, my

Gm7 | |
only friend through teenage nights, and

B♭ | |
everything I had to know I

Gm7 |**B♭**   F | |
heard it on my radio.   You

Verse 1   **Fadd9** | |
gave them all those old time stars, through

Gm⁷ | |
wars of worlds invaded by Mars. You

B♭ | |
made 'em laugh, you made 'em cry, you

Gm⁷ |B♭ F |Gm¹¹/F F |
made us feel like we could fly. Ra - dio. So

F | |
don't become some background noise, a

Fm⁶/A♭ | |
backdrop for the girls and boys who

B♭ | |
just don't know or just don't care, and

G⁷/B | |
just complain when you're not there. You

F/C | |
had your time, you had the power, you've

C⁷sus⁴ **C⁷** |**C⁹** **C⁷** |B♭ F |Gm⁷/F F |
yet to have your finest hour. Ra - dio. Ra - dio.

Chorus 1   **F⁷/E♭** |B♭ F |B♭ F |B♭ F |
All we hear is Radio ga ga, Radio goo goo, Radio ga ga.

F⁷/E♭ |B♭ F |B♭ F |
All we hear is Radio ga ga, Radio blah blah.

E♭ |B♭ C |
Radio what's new?

Dm |F/C C |Csus⁴ C |F |
Radio, someone still loves you!

| | | | | |
                                                We

Verse 2   **Fadd9** | |
watch the shows, we watch the stars, on

Gm⁷ | |
videos for hours and hours. We

B♭ | |
hardly need to use our ears, how

37

Gm⁷ | **B♭** **F** | **Gm¹¹/F** **F** |

music changes through the years.   Ra - dio. Let's

F | |

hope you never leave old friend, like

Fm⁶/A♭ | |

all good things on you we depend. So

B♭ | |

stick around 'cos we might miss you, when

G⁷/B | |

we grow tired of all this visual. You

F/C | |

had your time, you had the power, you've

C⁷sus4 **C⁷** | **C⁹** **C⁷** | **B♭** **F** | **Gm⁷/F** **F** |

yet to have your finest hour. Radio.   Ra - dio.

Chorus 2   *(as Chorus 1)*

Coda   **F** | | | |

All we hear is Radio ga ga, Radio goo goo, Radio ga ga.

| | | |

All we hear is Radio ga ga, Radio goo goo, Radio ga ga.

F⁷/E♭ | **B♭** **F** | **B♭** **F** | **E♭** |

All we hear is Radio ga ga, Radio blah blah. Radio what's new?

B♭ **C** | **Dm⁷** **C** | **C**sus4 **C** | **F** | ‖

Someone still   loves you.

Somebody To Love

Words and Music by
FREDDIE MERCURY

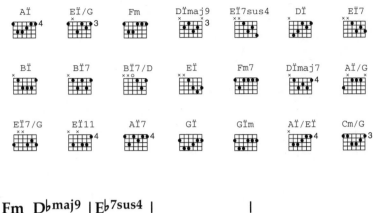

Intro

Freely

$\frac{4}{4}$ A♭ | E♭/G Fm D♭maj9 | E♭7sus4 | |
Can any - bo - dy   find me

D♭   E♭7 | A♭ |
somebody to   love?

| $\frac{12}{8}$ A♭ E♭/G Fm | D♭   E♭7 |
                                        Each

Verse 1

Moderately

A♭   E♭/G   Fm | A♭   B♭   E♭7 |
morning I get up, I die a little, can't barely stand on my feet. Take a

A♭ E♭/G Fm | B♭   E♭7 |
look in the mirror and cry, Lord, what you're doing to me. I have

A♭   B♭7   E♭ | B♭7/D E♭   D♭ |
spent all my years in believing you, but I just can't get no relief, Lord

Chorus 1

A♭ |
somebody, *somebody*, somebody, *somebody*,

$\frac{6}{8}$ E♭7/G Fm7 D♭maj7 |
can anybody find me

$\frac{12}{8}$ E♭7 | A♭   A♭/G | Fm D♭ | $\frac{6}{8}$ E♭7 |
        somebody to   love?   I work

Verse 2

$\frac{12}{8}$ A♭   E♭/G   Fm |
        hard ev'ry day of my life,

A♭   B♭7   E♭7 |
I work till I ache my bones. At the

A♭ E♭/G Fm |B♭7 |
end   I take home my hard earned pay all on my own. I get

A♭   B♭7   E♭ |
down on my knees and I start to pray 'til the

      B♭7/D   E♭   D♭ |
tears run down from my eyes, Lord

Chorus 2   A♭ |
somebody, *somebody*, somebody, *somebody*, can

     E♭7/G Fm7 D♭maj7 |
anybody   find   me

$^6_8$ E♭11 |$^{12}_8$ A♭ |A♭7 |D♭ |
   somebody to love?   Ev'ry day I

Interlude |G♭ |
try and I try, But ev'rybody wants to put me down, they

G♭m |B♭7 |
say I'm goin' crazy. They say I got a lot of water in my brain, got

        |E♭7 A♭/E♭ |$^6_8$ |
no common sense. I got nobody left to believe. Yeah, yeah, yeah, yeah.

Verse 3   A♭ Cm/G Fm   A♭ B♭7 E♭7
(Instrumental) $^{12}_8$| /. /.   /. /. |/. /. /. /. |

       A♭ Cm/G Fm   B♭7 E♭7 D♭
| /. /.   /. /. |/. /. /. /. |

       A♭ B♭7 E♭   B♭7/D E♭ D♭
| /. /. /. /. |/. /. /. /. |

Chorus 3   A♭ |
Ooh, somebody, somebody, can

     E♭7/G Fm7 D♭maj7 |
anybody   find   me

$^6_8$ E♭7 |$^{12}_8$ A♭ A♭/G |Fm   D♭ |$^6_8$ E♭7 |
       somebody to love?   Got no

Verse 4   A♭ E♭/G Fm |A♭   B♭7   E♭7 |

feel. I got no rhythm, I just keep losing my beat. I'm

A♭   E♭/G Fm |B♭7   E♭7 |

O.K. I'm alright, ain't gonna face no defeat. I just

A♭   B♭7   E♭ |

gotta get out of this prison cell, one

        B♭7/D E♭ D♭ | |

day I'm gonna be free, Lord.

Coda   N.C. | |

Find me somebody to love, find me somebody to love,

A♭ | |

find me somebody to love, find me somebody to love,

          | |

find me somebody to love, find me somebody to love,

          | |

find me somebody to love, find me somebody to love.

$\frac{6}{8}$ |$\frac{12}{8}$ |

       Find me somebody to love,

       |

find me somebody to love,

               |

somebody, somebody, somebody, somebody,

            | $\frac{6}{8}$ |

somebody, find me somebody, find me somebody to love. Can

$\frac{12}{8}$ A♭ E♭7/G Fm7 D♭maj7 | |

  anybody find me

N.C. | |

somebody to love?

A♭ A♭/G |Fm   D♭   E♭7 |

  Find me somebody to

A♭ A♭/G |Fm   D♭   E♭7 |

love! Find me somebody to

A♭ A♭/G |Fm   D♭   E♭7 |

love! Find me somebody to

A♭ | ‖

love! Find me, find me, find me, find me.

The Show Must Go On

Words and Music by
FREDDIE MERCURY, BRIAN MAY, ROGER TAYLOR AND JOHN DEACON

♩ = 84

Intro

Bm   B^sus2   B^sus4   Bm Bm/A

4/4 | / / / / | / / / / / |

G   G^add#11   Em/G G G/F#

| / / / / | / / / / / |

Em^7 Em^6   F#^sus4   F#

| / / / / | / / / / / |

Em A#dim/E |
Empty

Verse 1

Bm   B^sus2 | B^sus4   Bm |
spaces, what are we living for? Abandoned

G   G^add#11 | Em/G   G   G/F# |
places, I guess we know the score.

Em^7   Em^6 | F#^sus4   F# |
On and on, does anybody know what we are

Em   A#dim/E |
looking for?   Another

Bm B^sus2 | B^sus4   Bm |
hero, another mindless crime behind the

G   G^add#11 | Em/G   G   G/F# |
curtain in the   pantomime,

Em⁷   Em⁶ | F♯sus4   F♯ |

hold the line, does anybody want to take it any-

Em   G/A   G |

more? The show must go

Chorus 1

Bm   Bsus2 | Bsus4   Bm   Bm/A |

on,   the show must go

G   Gadd♯11 | Em/G   G |

on.   In-

Em⁷   Em⁶ | F♯sus4   F♯ |

side my heart is breaking, my make-up may be be flaking but my

Em A♯dim/E | Bm | F♯madd9 |

smile still   stays on.   Whatever

Verse 2

C♯m   C♯sus2 | C♯sus4   C♯m |

happens I leave it all to chance, another

A   Aadd♯11 | F♯m/A   A |

heartache another   failed romance.

F♯m⁷   F♯m⁶ | G♯sus4   G♯ |

On and on, does   anybody know what we are

F♯m   B♯dim/F♯ F♯m |

living for? I   guess I'm

C♯m   C♯sus2 | C♯sus4   C♯m |

learning, I must be warmer now, I'll soon be

A   Aadd♯11 | F♯m/A   A |

turning round the corner now. Out-

F♯m⁷   F♯m⁶ | G♯sus4   G♯ |

side the dawn is breaking, but inside the dark I'm aching

F♯m   D♯dim/F♯ | Em |

to be free.   The show must go

Chorus 2

Bm   B^{sus2} | B^{sus4}   Bm   Bm/A |
on,   the show must go

G   G^{add♯11} | Em/G   G |
on.   Ooh, in-

Em⁷   Em⁶ | F♯^{sus4}   F♯ |
side my heart is breaking, my make-up may be flaking but my

| Em   A♯^{dim}/E |
smile   still

Bm   B^{sus2} | B^{sus4}   Bm   Bm/A |
stays on.

G   G^{add♯11} | Em/G   G   G/F♯ |
Yeah,   yeah,   ooh,

Em⁷   Em⁶ | F♯^{sus4}   F♯ |
oh, ooh,   oh.

    Em   E^{dim}
| / / / / | / / / / |

Interlude

F   G/F | Em   Am   C^{maj7}/G |
My soul is painted like the wings of butterflies,

F   G/F | Em⁷   Am |
fairy tales of yesterday will grow but never die, I

C♯m^{7♭5}   A⁷/C♯ | D^{sus4}   D   Bm |
can fly.   My friends the show must go

Chorus 3

Bm   B^{sus2} | B^{sus4}   Bm |
on,   yeah,   the show must go

G   G^{add♯11} | Em/G   G   G/F♯ |
on.   I'll

Em⁷   Em⁶ | F♯^{sus4}   F♯ |
face it with a grin, I'm   never giving in, on

Em   A♯^{dim}/E |
with the show.

| Bm   B^{sus2}   B^{sus4}   Bm
| / / / / | / / / / |

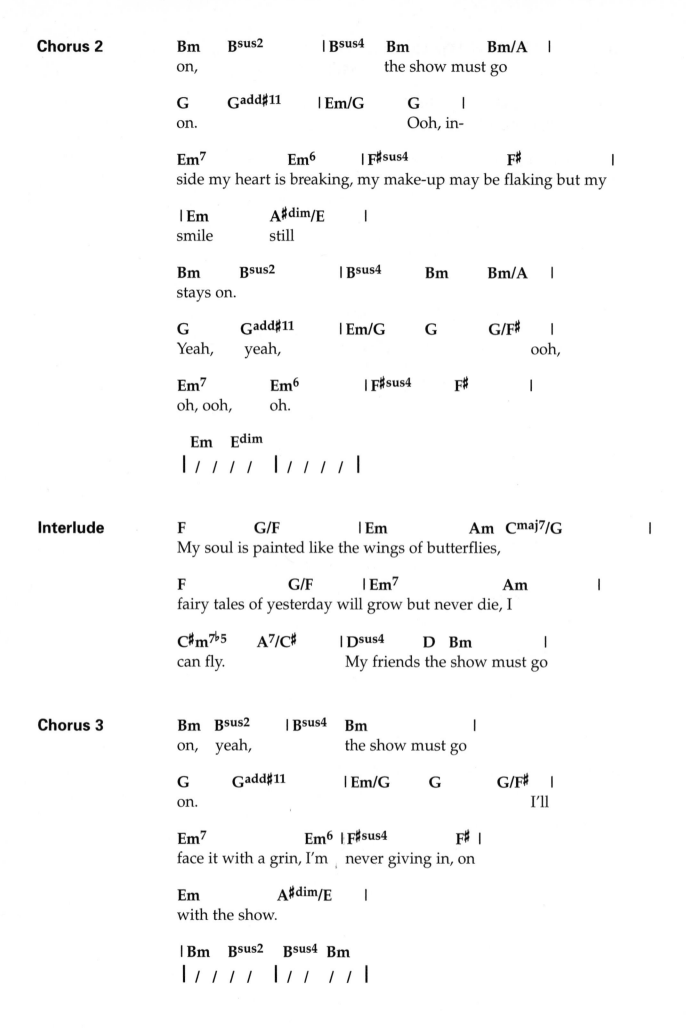

| G   G$^{add\sharp 11}$ | Em/G   G |

                                          Ooh I'll

Em^7 Em^6 | F$\sharp^{sus4}$ F$\sharp$ |

top the bill, I'll overkill, I have to find the will to carry on.

Em Em^7 Em^6

| / / /   / |

Coda   A$\sharp^{dim}$/E   Em^7 Bm

| / / / / | / / / / | $\frac{2}{4}$ / / | $\frac{4}{4}$ / / / / |

Bm^{add9}

| / / / / | / / / / | *(Repeat last bar to fade)*

Too Much Love Will Kill You

Words and Music by
BRIAN MAY, FRANK MUSKER AND ELIZABETH LAMERS

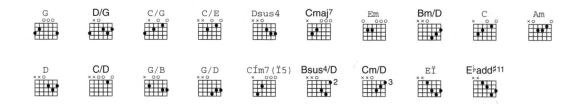

♩ = 78

Intro 4/4 G   D/G | C/G | G   D/G | C/E   Dˢᵘˢ⁴ |
                                                                      I'm just the pie-

Verse 1 G   Cᵐᵃʲ⁷ C | G   D/G |
ces of the man I   used to be,   too many

Em   Bm/D | C |
bitter tears are rainin' down on me.   I'm

Am   Em | Am   Em |
far away from home, and I've been facing this alone for much too

Dˢᵘˢ⁴   D | C/D |
long.   I feel like

G   C | G   D/G |
no-one ever told the truth to me, 'bout growin'

Em   Bm/D | C |
up and what a struggle it would be.   In my

Am   Em | Am   Em |
tangled state of mind, I've been lookin' back to find where I went

Dˢᵘˢ⁴   D | C/D |
wrong.

Chorus 1 G   C | Em   D |
Too much love will kill you if you can't make up your mind,

G   C | Em   D |
torn between the lover, and the love you leave behind. You're

G/B   **C**   **|G/D**   **C#7b5**   **|**
headed for disaster, 'cause you never read the signs,

G/D   **C/D**   **|G**   **D/G**   **|**
too much love will kill you ev'ry time.

C/G   **|G**   **D/G**   **|C/E**   **Dsus4**   **|**
                                              I'm just the

Verse 2   **G**   **Cmaj7 C**   **|G**   **D/G**   **|**
            shadow of the man I   used to be,   and it

Em   **Bm/D**   **|C**   **|**
seems like there's no way out of this for me.   I

Am   **Em**   **|Am**   **Em**   **|**
used to bring you sunshine, now all I ever do is bring you

Dsus4   **D**   **|C/D**   **|**
down.   How would it

G   **C**   **|G**   **D/G**   **|**
be if you were standing in my shoes? Can't you

Em   **Bm/D**   **|C**   **|**
see it's impossible to choose?   No

Am   **Em**   **|Am**   **Em**   **|**
there's no making sense of it, ev'ry way I go I have to

Dsus4   **D**   **|C/D**   **|**
lose.   Ooh.

Chorus 2   **G**   **C**   **|Em**   **D**   **|**
            Too much love will kill you just as surely as none at all. It'll

G   **C**   **|**
drain the power that's in you, make you

Em   **D**   **|**
plead and scream and crawl. And the

G/B   **C**   **|G/D**   **C#7b5** **|**
pain will make you crazy, you're the victim of your crime,

G/D   **C/D**   **|G**   **D/G**   **|**
too much love will kill you ev'ry time.

  C/G   **G**   **D/G C** **Dsus4 D**
| / / / / | / / / / | / / / /   / |

Interlude   G   C   G   D/G Em   B^{sus4}/D Bm/D C

| / / / / | / / / / | / / / | / | / / / / |

Am   Em   Am   Em   D^{sus4} D   C/D

| / / / / | / / / / | / / / / / | / / / / |

Coda

G   C | Em   D |
Too much love will kill you, it will make your life a lie, yes

G   C | Em   D |
too much love will kill you, and you won't understand why. You'll

G/B   C | G/D   C$^{\sharp 7\flat 5}$ |
give your life, you'll sell your soul, but here it comes again,

$\frac{2}{4}$ | $\frac{4}{4}$ G/D | Cm/D |
                too much love will kill you   in the

E$\flat$ E$\flat$add$^{\sharp}$11 | E$\flat$ E$\flat$add$^{\sharp}$11 | G   ‖
end,   in the end.

48

Under Pressure

Words and Music by
FREDDIE MERCURY, BRIAN MAY, ROGER TAYLOR, JOHN DEACON AND DAVID BOWIE

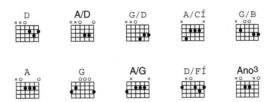

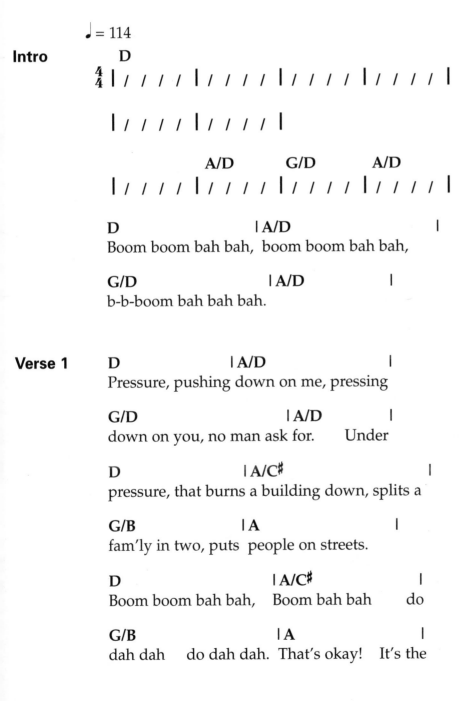

♩ = 114

Intro

D

4/4

A/D   G/D   A/D

D |A/D |
Boom boom bah bah, boom boom bah bah,

G/D |A/D |
b-b-boom bah bah bah.

Verse 1

D |A/D |
Pressure, pushing down on me, pressing

G/D |A/D |
down on you, no man ask for.   Under

D |A/C♯ |
pressure, that burns a building down, splits a

G/B |A |
fam'ly in two, puts people on streets.

D |A/C♯ |
Boom boom bah bah,   Boom bah bah   do

G/B |A |
dah dah   do dah dah. That's okay!   It's the

Chorus 1   G   A/G |G   A/G |
terror of knowing what this world is about.

                G   A/G |G   A/G |
Watching some good friends screaming 'Let me out!' Pray to-

                G   A/G |G A/G |
morrow takes me higher. Pressure

                D/F# |G   A |
on people, people on   streets.

                D | | | |
Do do do, bah bah bah bah bah,   okay.

Verse 2   D |A/D |
Pressure, pushing down on me, pressing

                G/D |A/D |
down on you, no man ask for.   Under

                D |A/C# |
pressure, that burns a building down, splits a

                G/B |A |
fam'ly in two, puts people on the streets.

                D |A/C# |
Bah bah bah,   bah bah bah   bah

                G/B |A |
bah bah   bah bah bah. That's okay! It's the

Chorus 2   G   A/G |G   A/G |
terror of knowing what this world is about.

                G   A/G |G   A/G |
Watching some good friends screaming 'Let me out!' Pray to-

                G   A/G |G A/G |
morrow takes me higher. Pressure

                D/F# |G   A | |
on people, people on   streets.   Turned a-

Interlude   G |C |
way from it all like a blind man,

                G |C |
sat on a fence, but it don't work. Keep

G |C |A^{no3rd} A |
coming up with love, but it's so slashed and torn. Why?   Why?

F |G/F |F |G/F |
Why?

A^{no3rd} | |
Love, love, love, love.   In-

A | G |
sanity laughs under pressure we're cracking. Can't we

D |G   A   G |
give ourselves one more chance? Why can't we

D |G   A   G |
give love that one more chance? Why can't we

D |G   A   G |
give love, give love, give love, give love,

D |A/C♯ |
give love, give love, give love, give love? 'Cause

G/B |A |D |A/C♯ |
love's such an old fashioned word, and love dares you to

G/B |A |D |A/C♯ |
care for the people on the edge of the night, and love

G/B |A |G |A/G |
dares you to change our way of caring   about ourselves.

G |A/G |G |A/G |
This is our last dance. This is our last dance.

D/F♯ |G   A |
This is ourselves under

Coda   D | | |G/D A/D |
pressure,   under pressure,

D | |G   A |
pressure.

| / / / / | / / / / | *(repeat last 2 bars to fade)*

We Are The Champions

Words and Music by
FREDDIE MERCURY

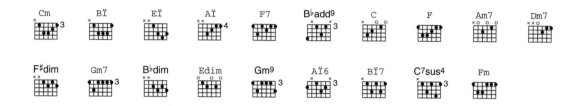

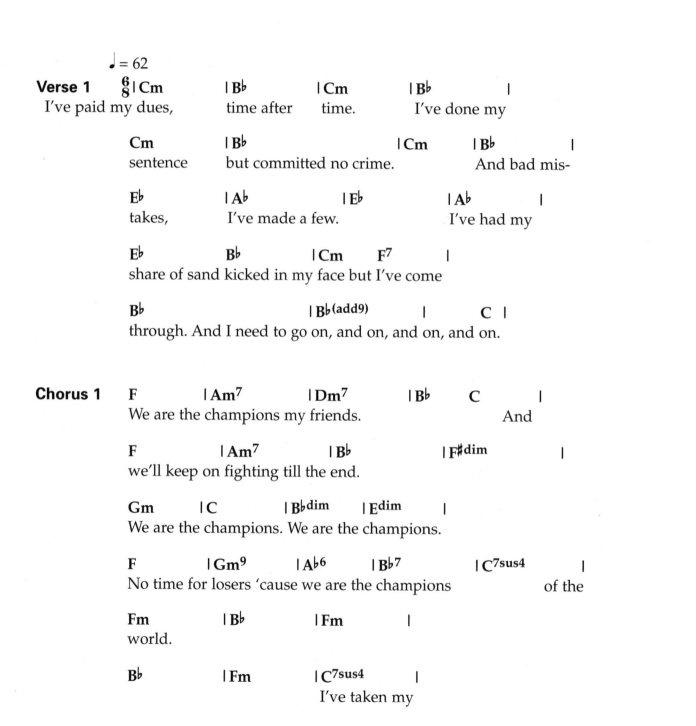

♩ = 62

Verse 1   6/8 | Cm | B♭ | Cm | B♭ |
I've paid my dues,   time after   time.   I've done my

Cm | B♭ | Cm | B♭ |
sentence   but committed no crime.   And bad mis-

E♭ | A♭ | E♭ | A♭ |
takes,   I've made a few.   I've had my

E♭   B♭ | Cm   F⁷ |
share of sand kicked in my face but I've come

B♭ | B♭(add9) | C |
through. And I need to go on, and on, and on, and on.

Chorus 1   F | Am⁷ | Dm⁷ | B♭   C |
We are the champions my friends.   And

F | Am⁷ | B♭ | F♯dim |
we'll keep on fighting till the end.

Gm | C | B♭dim | Edim |
We are the champions. We are the champions.

F | Gm⁹ | A♭⁶ | B♭⁷ | C⁷sus4 |
No time for losers 'cause we are the champions   of the

Fm | B♭ | Fm |
world.

B♭ | Fm | C⁷sus4 |
                    I've taken my

Verse 2
Cm | B♭ | Cm | B♭ |
bows   and my curtain calls.   You brought me

Cm | B♭ |
fame and fortune and ev'rything that goes with it, I thank you

Cm | B♭ |
all.   But it's been no bed of ros-

E♭ | A♭ | E♭ | A♭ |
es,   no pleasure cruise.   I consider it a

E♭   B♭ | Cm   F⁷ |
challenge before the whole human race and I ain't gonna

B♭ | B♭(add9) | C |
lose. And I need to go on, and on, and on, and on.

Chorus 2
F | Am⁷ | Dm⁷ | B♭   C |
We are the champions my friends.   And

F | Am⁷ | B♭ | F♯dim |
we'll keep on fighting till the end.

Gm | C | B♭dim | Edim |
We are the champions. We are the champions.

F | Gm⁹ | A♭⁶ | B♭⁷ | C⁷sus4 |
No time for losers 'cause we are the champions   of the

Chorus 3
F | Am⁷ | Dm⁷ | B♭   C |
We are the champions my friends.   And
(world.)

F | Am⁷ | B♭ | F♯dim |
we'll keep on fighting till the end.

Gm | C | B♭dim | Edim |
We are the champions. We are the champions.

F | Gm⁹ | A♭⁶ | B♭⁷ | C⁷sus4   ‖
No time for losers 'cause we are the champions

You're My Best Friend

Words and Music by
JOHN DEACON

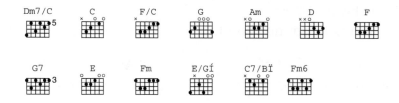

♩ = 116

Intro

       C   Dm⁷/C   C

$\frac{4}{4}$ | / / / / | / / / / | / / / / | / / / / |

Verse 1

Dm⁷/C |**C** |
Ooh, you make me live.   What-

F/C |**C** |
ever this world can give to me. It's

Dm⁷/C |**C** |
you, you're all I see.

Dm⁷/C |**C** |
Ooh, you make me live now, honey,

Dm⁷/C |**C**   **G** |
ooh, you make me live.

Am   **D** | **F** |
Ooh, you're the best friend that I

   G⁷ |**C**   **G** |
ever had. I've been with you such a

Am   **D** | **F** |
long time, you're my sunshine and I want

   G |**E**   **Am** |$\frac{2}{4}$**G** |$\frac{4}{4}$**F** |
you to know that my feelings are true, I   really love   you.

Chorus1

```
Fm                IC                              |
Oh, you're my best friend.

                        IDm⁷/C                  |
                        Ooh, you make me live.

C      E/G♯      IAm   C7/B♭          |
Ooh,  I've been  wan - dering round,

F                              IFm⁶                  |
But I still come back to you,                    In

G            E/G♯    IAm          D      IG              |
rain or shine you've stood by me, girl, I'm  happy at home,

               IC                    |                |
you're my best friend.
```

Verse 2

```
Dm⁷/C                   IC                      |
Ooh, you make me live.              When-

F/C               IC              |
ever this world is cruel to me, I got

Dm⁷/C                  IC                    |
you to help me forgive.

Dm⁷/C                  IC                    |
Ooh, you make me live now, honey,

Dm⁷/C                        IC          G          |
ooh, you make me live.

Am             D   IF                    |
Ooh, you're the first one. When things

        G⁷        IC       G      |
turn out bad.    You know I'll never be

Am                 D   IF                  |
lonely. You're my on - ly one and I love

    G        IE    Am     |
the things, I really love the

²₄G           I⁴₄F                  |
  things that   you do.
```

Chorus 2   *(As Chorus 1)*

Coda   **Fm**^{6} | **C** |
Ooh,

Fm^6 | **C** |
ooh, you're my best friend,

Dm^7**/C** | **C** |
ooh, you make me live.

Dm^7**/C** |
Ooh, you're my best friend.

G C   G C   G C
| / / / / | / / / / | / / / / | / / / / | / / / / ‖

Printed by Halstan & Co. Ltd., Amersham, Bucks., England